Heart to Heart

Worlds Apart

Thank you for
making a
difference!

Peg

ISBN: 0-9676501-0-0

Cover Watercolors by Krystyn Stanley
Cover Graphic Design by Jared Johnson
Text layout by Shannon Dixon
Printing:
Press America
Distribution:
Granite Publishing & Distribution
1- (800) 574-5779

This book is dedicated in memory of
Veronica Chipendo

Thanks. Where do I begin? So many people have helped, and to everyone who has helped and to everyone who wanted to help I give a most hearty thank you. But to three in particular without whom I know this would not have been possible.

To my editor, Steve Cook, who in the beginning I know must have read my work and wondered if it was possible. But he caught the vision and wanted to stick with me to the end. Thank you Steve!

To my husband, Scott, who just smiled quietly to himself when I announced, "I am going to write a book." Yet he supported me all the way. I love you Scott!

And the most importantly of all: to my dear God in heaven above. If it wasn't for the constant thought He planted in my heart, I would have given up long ago, believe me it was so real I couldn't get it out no matter how I tried. He knew my imperfections better than anyone else, but He also knew what had to be done, so each time I came to a closed door he opened it for me. And every time I wanted to quit, He wouldn't let me. Thank you Heavenly Father!

Contents

We all have dreams,
the kind you have when you're awake,
you believe that if they'd come true,
you would be the happiest person in the world.
And sometimes . . . when they do . . . you are!

1

"The Feeling Side"

Just inside the border I asked Joy and Sandy to walk on ahead. I needed a few moments to myself. Moments to appreciate, moments of saying, hey, somebody pinch me, I can't believe this is all true; and moments of thanks.

Here I am in Zambia. I had imagined this day for twenty years. The stories I had heard were now becoming more than just words. It was every bit as beautiful and more. It was also every bit as poor.

I could tell a difference the minute we crossed the border. It didn't seem possible, but my surroundings got even poorer. Zimbabwe was poor, but nothing had prepared me for this. The Zambian border post was more a shack than a building. The people wore clothing hand-washed so many times that they could no longer get them clean, and they had no way to fix the threadbare holes. Nobody wore shoes. The poverty was simply overwhelming.

The taxis stood by, anxiously waiting to take anyone with money to wherever they needed to go, but most people walked. Taxis? Yes, they were taxis, but they all had broken windshields, with the body rusted through, a rope holding the trunk shut and bald tires. To look at these vehicles you wondered how they could even run. Maybe dirt was easier on tires than pavement. Now I could see why they told me at the embassy, "Once you get up there you can take a taxi all day for just a dollar." In Zimbabwe one American dollar was worth thirty-eight Zimbabwe dollars. But now as I crossed the border a dollar was worth four hundred Zambian dollars.

Crossing into Zambia, I noticed the people looked different from those in Zimbabwe. They looked more like . . . well, they just looked more like Tansy and Nkosi to me. Most of the people I had talked to in Zimbabwe had never been in Zambia. They couldn't afford to pay the high cost to cross over and usually had no desire to visit the poorer country. These two countries were split by a giant river gorge. There were heavy fines for any one caught crossing the river. I found it fascinating that they would stand alongside the river and wave to the foreigners on the other bank, and yet never set foot on their neighbor's soil.

This was Dr. Livingstone's favorite place on earth. He had explored all through Africa only to end up here, where he died. This was the place he loved. Perhaps it was the majesty of the Falls, or the kindness of the local natives. I could relate to his feelings, as there was something here, something very peaceful, something that could make you never want to return to the old rat race again.

There would be more time to reflect later. I ran to catch up with Joy and Sandy. I met them as they were about to enter what we thought was the park on the Zambian side. Both countries had a view of Victoria Falls. The Falls were named by Dr. Livingstone for Queen Victoria. Both countries had a so-called "park" located next to the Falls. On the Zimbabwe side there were wood buildings complete with restrooms (flush toilets), a museum, and a gate marking the entrance to the park. They even had a large stone statue of Dr. Livingstone. As you walk down to the Falls, there were overlooks scattered along the trail. Each overlook had a fence to protect you from falling off the edge.

The Zambian side was quite different. There were no signs, no gates, nothing that would indicate that you had entered the park. Oh, they had a little building where you paid your fee, but it was a tiny grass hut. We walked down a lonely dirt path and almost missed it. Then out of the blue, a man inside called to us.

"'Ello, madam, ten zims, please." We looked at each other and said, "This must be the park gate." We gave him our ten zims, and he went to write it down in a book, but couldn't find a pen. While he fumbled around looking for one, another man came into the hut. He kept staring at us. I was quite used to being stared at by this point of my journey, but Sandy seemed to be getting nervous. With five of us in this little hut it was getting very crowded. He was taking too long counting our money, and there was no one else around. She started to fumble through her purse searching for her lighter. The man who we assumed was in charge said to the other man, "Get the lady a match."

He promptly left in search of a match. All day we hadn't seen another white person. We wondered if this was true for them too. Maybe they enjoyed seeing us white women tourists scared and were milking this for all it was worth. Soon the man came running back and handed her a single match. She thanked him, but she had already found her lighter. I stood there watching them stare as she lit up her cigarette.

On this trip I had learned that staring does not mean something vicious is about to happen. It is not meant as a threat. It is done more out of curiosity, curiosity out of seeing things you don't see everyday, and we were as guilty of it as they were. Once again, they were just trying to be helpful and it took us time to trust them. These people had time and plenty of it. No one was ever in a hurry and this time was no different. The man who took our money said, "You can go in now."

There were no pamphlets, no fences, no signs, just a dirt path leading down to the Falls. As we stepped outside, Sandy said, "I thought he was going to rob us for sure."

Once inside the park, we saw a broken-down statue with just the base left standing. The words were so faded they couldn't be read. We walked on and the vegetation started to get extremely dense. We had to bushwhack our way to the Falls. Since you could hear the Falls long before you could see them, we used the sound as our guide. We kept taking paths that would lead us closer to the sound. Finally when we arrived at our first lookout; we were awestruck. Here we were, merely a stone's throw away from the great, majestic Falls. This was the closest we had been to the Falls; right away we named this the "feeling side."

You got a better view of the mile and a half length of the Falls from the other side, so we called it the "seeing side."

On this, the "feeling side," there were no fences up to protect you from falling off the slippery edge. The falling of the water created a mist, the mist created a constant rain, and in no time you were completely drenched. Now with the water rolling down our hair and dumping into our eyes, it was difficult to see. This, coupled with the mist creating the perfect environment for moss to grow on the rocks, made for an awesome sight, yet extremely dangerous. We began to wonder how many people had tried to get closer for a better look, maybe for a fantastic picture, and . . . well, we didn't want to think about that.

"THE FEELING SIDE"

It is so hard to describe this to anyone. Maybe they could imagine the vibrations, as the ground literally shook from tons of water dumping over the sides and falling all the way to the ground. Maybe they could even imagine the sound of constant thunder so loud you had to shout at each other to be heard. But there could be no way you could ever imagine the sights. The rainbows hovering over the mists, brilliantly colored from the reflection of the shining sun, the thick, vivid-green vegetation, created by a constant falling rain, completely engulfing you and remaining virtually unspoiled by structures created by man. Then watching the waterfall down a gorge so deep you couldn't see the bottom. No, there are just some things a picture will never do justice to.

We planned on staying longer, but the more overlooks we went to, the more we noticed two men right behind us. We knew we were being followed. We imagined that we could be robbed and then pushed over the edge, never to be seen again. Soon we became so uncomfortable we decided we had better leave.

As we left the park we walked toward the town of Livingstone. I had told my friends about the cheap crafts available here, so we were on the look out for people selling hand-carved souvenirs. I had already given away almost everything I thought I could part with, but I had a one hundred rand bill (about seventeen U.S. dollars) left just for souvenirs.

Walking down the street we saw the usual items being sold, veggies, bottled water, and fruit. Nkosi had told me that the Zambian people needed the tourists so badly and the South African government had money so they made a deal. The Zambian government gave land to the South African government to build two fancy hotels. The South Africans would make the money from the hotels and hopefully the hotels would bring the much-needed tourists to Zambia. A good deal for both of them.

The more we walked, the more the poverty tore at our hearts. Soon we came to a giant tent. Several men came running out exclaiming, "Madam, come see."

"Madam, come buy."

"Madam, do you have any pins?"

"Pins?"

They held up an imaginary sheet of paper and began to mimic writing on it with a pen.

"Oh, you want a *pen.*"

"Yes, madam, pens."

I looked in my purse, and as is usually the case, I didn't have a single one. I wished I could have known, for back home in Cape Town I had left three brand-new packages of pens in my suitcase. But how could I have guessed these people would want pens?

I went inside the tent and soon fell in love with everything I saw. There were necklaces with each bead hand-carved, even the clasp, so that each side wound perfectly into the other. There were bowls carved in the shape of the African continent with a giraffe bending down, his long legs spread apart trying to get a drink out of it, all made out of one piece of wood. Incredible the talent to be found here!---not one of these was a product of mass production. Soon I had spent my hundred rands, as I had not the heart to negotiate a better price, seeing the poverty that surrounded me.

Now out of money, I turned around to leave, when a man came up to me and said, "Madam, come sit down, we talk." I tried to explain to him that I had spent all of my money.

"Madam, there must be something in your purse maybe I would like, let's make deals."

Then he pulled up two tree stumps and motioned for me to come back inside and sit down.

I opened my purse and looked inside. These days I was traveling light. But, oh well, out of curiosity, I went inside. As I was being tempted to trade with these men, I remembered seeing a big sign as we came into Zambia, which read, "Absolutely no trading. Severe fines enforced." I was not totally sure what that meant, but I had a pretty good idea. It probably referred to what I was about to do: don't trade your belongings, and pay with cash. I was struggling with that when another man said, "Madam, I like your combs."

"My combs?"

"The ones in your hair."

Now I remembered the plastic combs I had bought at K-Mart for fifty-nine cents.

"Madam, what do you want for your combs?" pointing to the blanket covered with woodcarvings.

Okay, so that's how it started. First my combs, then my lipstick, then my chapstick, anything I had in my purse. Everything was of value to these fellows. I would hold up something and a man down the line of vendors would say, "Let me see that."

I would take it down to him and he would look it over and then say, "Okay, what do you want for it?"

Then when I thought I had nothing left, a man pointed at me and said, "Your shirt, madam, your shirt. What do you want for your shirt?"

I said, "No way! You can't have my shirt!"

I thought, What do they expect? I do have my limitations, you know. He quickly said, "No, no! Not that shirt." Then pointing to the extra shirt I had tied around my waist, he said, "That shirt."

Oh, I had totally forgotten about that shirt. I looked down and a comb with a zebra head for a handle caught my attention. I had bought the shirt at Savers, a secondhand store, for a dollar. Just when I thought I'd be cheating him if I traded the shirt for the comb, he said, "Madam, this is not a comb, this is a fork, and it belongs with this spoon. It is a set and you cannot break up the set."

Now I was really stuck because I had nothing left to trade. I had to reply, "I'm sorry, I can't buy your set. It is too nice for that shirt."

"But, madam, what about your shoes?"

My shoes? I thought about this. I had also bought my shoes at Savers for three dollars. They were very worn, and because of the Falls, very wet. They couldn't have been worth much, if anything. But, if he wanted them, then okay.

"Are you sure you want my shoes?"

"Oh, yes, madam."

"Okay."

I traded my shirt and shoes for a lovely hand-carved zebra-headed fork and spoon. I'm not sure who made out best on this one.

When I met back up with Joy and Sandy, they could not believe I had traded my shoes, and as we started our walk back, neither could I.

The walk back was hot with the sun directly overhead, and no relief in sight. It made the walk back to the border seem longer than I had remembered. I tried to stay on the dirt, as the sidewalks were too hot. Actually, it could have been worse if there had been stickers and thorns, but because of so much barefoot traffic, there weren't any. I was used to walking without shoes. My friends back home would tease me because they knew I hated wearing shoes, and at any opportunity I would take them off.

Before we could get to the border post, we had to first pass the police station. As we approached the police station, I got real nervous. If they tried to fine me, there's no way I could pay. I tried to walk along as fast as I could, trying not to draw attention to my feet.

Just then, as if on cue, a family of monkeys stepped out of the bush and almost stepped on us. They were a rough looking group, all dirty and mangy, most of their fur was matted, some even had battle scars. They were nothing like the

8

clean, smooth monkeys at the zoo. My entire trip I had wanted to see monkeys. I thought about getting out my camera, but I didn't dare, thinking this would draw more attention to myself. Out stepped one of the biggest monkeys of the group, and he began to walk towards me. Now he was so close I could have reached out and touched him. Could this be? He was actually staring at my feet. Now the thought came to me that a dog can tell if you're afraid. This monkey kind of reminded me of a dog. So I tried my hardest not to show I was afraid. He stared at me, and I stared at him, neither one of us wanted to be the first to move. I had this funny feeling that the policemen were staring at us too. After what seemed like minutes, but was probably more like seconds, the big ape just kind of grunted and turned around to join the others. I looked over to see the other monkeys standing in the middle of a crowd of people waiting to cross the border. No one paid any attention to the monkeys; they were sitting there waiting as if they would like to cross too.

Once inside the border post things went smoothly. Now all we had to do was walk back across that long bridge which connected Zambia to Zimbabwe. Sandy and Joy's friends would be there, waiting for us with the car. They had a good laugh when they saw me coming, wearing no shoes.

Back at the lodge I had so much to think about. Staying alone has its advantages. Unless you are completely alone, and alone for a considerable amount of time, you can't possibly have the quality time you need to contemplate life.

Well, contemplating is just what I was doing. This past week I had seen people so poor that they lived in a one-room shack with only a few tree stumps and a table for their furniture. Some, living under these conditions, seemed warm and happy. They were eager to show me their families full of small children, who filled the air with laughter. Others were angry with their circumstances, angry at the world, not just angry, jealous---jealous of anyone who had more. How could people living under the same conditions have such different attitudes? Was there a time in my life when material possessions were less important? A time when life was simpler? Was I happier then? I was also thinking about my very dear friend, Tansy Manjani, and how knowing her had changed the course of my life. I closed my eyes and began to think back.

When I'm old, when I'm forgotten,
sitting alone in my rocking chair,
"where's my joy?" you ask. In my memories!

2

Toads

I started as far back as my memory would take me. Do these early years have anything to do with what I would become in the future? And just how early do you start to become who you are?

I don't know why, but the first thing to come to my mind was Mr. Sorensen's apple orchard. Not only the orchard, but also Mr. Sorensen's face, that grouchy old face. He was so grouchy that sneaking apples from his orchard was the scariest, and yet the most challenging, of all the games we kids could dream up. If he caught us, we would be gonners for sure! I can still remember running with all the energy adrenaline gives you when you're scared, then turning around and seeing his ornery old red face, all wrinkled up with sweat pouring down, hollering with the last bit of energy he had left.

"I'm telling you kids for the last time. Stay out of my orchard."

Even at church he was ornery; I never saw him smile. I figured that's just what happens to you when you get old. You just keep getting more mean and more miserable. I didn't want to get old; the fact is I started thinking of ways I could avoid it altogether.

Then I met Ruby Compton. Ruby was eighty or ninety, I can't remember which because at my age I didn't think there was any difference between the two. Ruby was the sweetest, kindest, happiest old lady I had ever met. Everything I said made her laugh. This always made me feel so good inside. For each dandelion we dug out of her grass, she always gave us a penny apiece, a sizeable sum at our age. I soon started to compare the two old souls. Using my limited amount of wisdom, I finally had to ask, "Ruby, what makes you so happy all the time, when all the other old people seem so grouchy?"

To that she let out a hearty laugh. The laugh then turned into a smile and she replied, "Honey, ornery old people are just ornery people who got ornerier, and sweet old people are just sweet people who got sweeter."

Then she leaned down real close to my ear and whispered, "Now maybe that's true, and maybe it isn't. But this I want you to remember and never forget. You will spend your whole life trying to acquire things, and that's all right, but happy are the people who know when they have enough."

Well, thirty-five years later I have come to realize that there's more to it than that. But those two thoughts, coming from a woman who I thought was so wise, stuck with me.

As I thought of Edgemont Elementary, I saw it just the same as the day I left it. I could see the sixth-grade window I had thrown the baseball through and got sent to the principal's office. There were the tetherball poles where I would run down as soon as the bell rang, hoping to be the first in line to play.

The hopscotch and the four squares were still painted on the blacktop. It was all there: my childhood. That sweet, innocent, almost lost, almost forgotten childhood.

So much had changed, yet my memory conjured up images, clear images, clear to the point of what color my clothes were on the first day of school those many years ago.

As I looked down the street, in my mind I didn't see every house looking the same. True, each house was built with the same exact blueprints, yet every home belonged to a family, a unique family, giving that home its own personality.

My home was the "growing things" home. Although it had just a small yard, my mom was always trying something new. She had a passion for growing things, all kinds of things. Anyone born with this passion knows that half the things you plant die. Maybe nature does this on purpose just so people with this passion get to keep trying and never run out of space to try in.

Well, I was born with it too. I say "born with it" because from my first recollection I spent as much time in the flower beds, on the grass, and in the vegetable patch, as any kid in the house. Anytime my mom would say, "Do you kids want an inside or an outside job?" there would be no question in my mind: "Outside."

My mom's all-time favorite things were her flowers. She had so many, but not the same common ones that everyone else had. She was always looking for something new, something different. Because of her many varieties, I had much to choose from to come up with my favorites. Favorites like snapdragons that if you pinched them just right their mouths would open. Bleeding hearts, they always made me sad because mom said they were people's broken hearts all lined up in a row and just lying there bleeding. Peonies, because they were so big and so fluffy. Oh, to smell the white ones was heaven on earth.

I was not, however, a child who liked to spend much time at home. We lived at the end of a dead-end street and next to our house was a big open field maybe three miles square. I loved to get with my neighborhood friends and play in that field. The wild grass grew way above my head. We called it "the Jungle." We would stomp down the grass and make narrow tunnels running through it. You could get lost in that field. I know, because one year I took Ward Lawson's Sunday shoe and threw it way out there somewhere. I got sent to my room for a whole day because no one could ever find it.

We had the most fun designing grass huts. Each year the huts got nicer and roomier. Then one year we decided we would attempt to dig a basement first. If we could get the hole deep enough it would have a nice, cool dirt floor, and we would use grass for the roof. Perfect! However, the digging was harder than we thought it would be. On the second day, Lavon got hit in the head with a shovel and refused to help anymore. That hurt us, she was our main man and could outdig any of us. Now with little choice left we had to give up. So we just pushed all the grass down in a circle and called it our "hut." We even hung up paper pictures on the stalks of grass left standing.

As much fun as the Jungle was, the real lifeblood of my childhood was "the River." In reality it was a muddy fifteen-foot-wide irrigation ditch. The canal ran from the top of my street down through the back lots of the homes facing ours, crossed the field, and then disappeared in a tunnel running under the road. Where it ended up none of us kids knew because we weren't allowed to go past the road.

Although at the time I was too young to understand the real reasons for the survival of life in that canal, my seasons revolved around that life.

Winter was still, quiet, and all life seemed dead. I always stood in awe wondering where the toads went when winter snows blanketed the ground and the tiny ponds in the canal were frozen solid.

But each March and April the miracle of life reappeared as if on cue. The warm spring winds and the longer days of sunshine began to melt the puddles left behind last fall. First came the elusive water-skeeters skeeting across the glassy surface, keeping just beyond the reach of the boy or girl trying to catch them. The skeeters were followed by polliwogs, their long hibernation over. Millions of polliwogs! The water seemed alive with them as they wiggled back and forth each time you came near.

Our long winter of hibernation was over too, and with the return of the polliwogs came the migration of the children back to the canal. They came from all over the neighborhood. This was our favorite time of year. With school almost out, and the long summer days ahead, our total freedom was just around the corner.

With the advent of June, I could spend all day long outside. This was real living! A group of us neighbor kids always hung out together: Lavon, Michael, Gary, Ward, even my two sisters, Glenda and Laura. We'd grab our cups, bottles, and buckets and race to the canal. It was each man for himself. You could keep as many as you could catch, so somehow it didn't seem quite fair when one year some kid turned up with a store-bought goldfish net.

It was that rush to catch a living thing that made us lose our senses. Even though our parents tried to make us take back what we had caught before the tiny creatures died, I'm sure we kids helped to keep those toad populations down.

With containers filled, we'd run along home to release our catch into old fish tanks, wash tubs, and wading pools, all filled with water from our hose. It didn't occur to us to lug home some buckets of pond water; if so, more of the toads probably would have lived.

Next came the task of coaxing them to eat. We tried everything from bread to goldfish food. Surprisingly, some made it to adulthood. Watching them change from polliwogs to full-grown toads was spellbinding. First one arm, then another, then a back leg, then its counterpart, all popping out from this clear, bag-like structure that enveloped their bodies. You could see the tiny arms and hands through the bag long before they popped through. It was all I could do to keep myself from trying to help them out. Finally, the last of their wonders, their tail would drop off. *Voila!* Magic! A tiny, perfectly formed toad! They were so cute. Then, at our parents' insistence, came the heroic march back to the canal to free them.

As June wore on and the days grew hotter, more water was released into the canal. With the water level so high, the toads were forced to seek new homes and food on the banks. They would go in search of food at night, hiding from the fierce sun during the day. Many a morning I awoke to find smashed toads on the street or the lucky ones alive in our grass. I loved the challenge of finding their hiding places.

In order to stay close to the water, their favorite stomping grounds were in the little hollows the lapping water had cut back into the banks. I would lie down on my stomach and reach far back into the darkness, hoping to be rewarded with the feel of a rough and bumpy, fat and squishy toad. Sometimes they were within reach; sometimes they were perched too far back for my short arms. Catching toads was one of the first of hundreds of times in my life I wished I was bigger.

At night, all summer long, the croaking of toads filled the air. A few times my dad took me up to the canal with a flashlight in hand. What an adventure it was to listen in total darkness for the source of their sounds, sneak up on them, and switch on the light. Flooded with brightness, there puffing out its cheeks, staring right at us, sat a saucepan-size toad, startled

16

by our intrusion. I loved catching toads and was one of the best at it!

One day sometime in July there came a knock at the door. It was pretty early in the morning, so I was the only one up. There on my porch stood four boys. One was real tall and skinny, the second looked sort of familiar, the third was red-haired and freckled, and the last I recognized all too well: Randy Bodell. He didn't know me, but his reputation as a bully easily preceded him. I at least knew enough to be scared of him.

The tall one nodded at me. "We heard you're pretty good at catchin' toads."

"Yeah, well, pretty good."

Then came the reason for their visit. "We want you to find us some."

All at once Randy piped up, "Come on, you guys, she ain't nothin' but a shrimp!"

To that challenge, I growled out a response that left them gaping: "Oh yeah! I'll find you some."

I had just finished my first year of school where I had quickly learned who the bullies were and their methods for getting what they wanted. Now even though I didn't like it and obviously hadn't thought it out all too clearly (a habit which has followed me much of my life), I grabbed my shoes, hollered to my sister, "Tell mom I'll be right back," and headed off for the canal.

I was walking a ways ahead of the boys, thinking to myself that in order to prove my toad-catching powers, I had to find a toad. We walked for what seemed like a long time. Then Randy's voice broke the silence. "I told ya she's no good at findin' toads. Come on, let's go."

I really was afraid of him, but I so badly wanted to show him up. Suddenly the big boy turned towards Randy and shouted,

"Well, you haven't found us any, so shut up!"

Now I was worried they were scaring away all the toads.

"I'm going to run up ahead," I said, "I'll call to you when I have one."

Then as I trudged on, kicking along the canal banks, I remembered a gigantic pipe that was buried in the ground next to a head gate. Originally installed to provide room so a handle could be turned that would open the gate for irrigation, it lay not far ahead; I had found toads there before.

Like a giant toad, my heart seemed like it was climbing up into my throat. I prayed, "Please put a toad in there."

Reaching the spot, I threw myself down onto my stomach and stretched my hand down through the opening. I can still remember the soft, lumpy texture of that big ol' toad. Yes! I struggled to get my hand around it, then hoisted it up. Oh, it was a beaut!

"Hey! I found one!" I yelled to the boys.

They all came running. "Hey, she *can* find toads!"

Randy began to whine, "That ain't nothin.' Everyone knows there's toads in there! Bet you can't find another one."

So that's how the rest of the day went. I kept finding impressively large toads, and Randy kept getting madder. What a day!

When fall came the water flow slowed to a trickle. In many spots, standing water mixed with rotting leaves and dead insects created a bacteria-laden mud. It was thick, black, gooey, and *very* smelly. It was always hard to see summer come to an end, but I suppose in some ways even school could be an adventure.

For my first day back at school, I had picked out my favorite outfit to wear: a gray corduroy jumper and a white blouse with puffy sleeves, some matching gray knee socks, and some black and white oxford shoes. Adding to the stunning effect I was sure my attire would have on my peers, I even let my mom do what she wanted with my hair. Boy, was I stylin,' or what?

Now, to get to my school you could go the long way to the end of my street, across two other streets, and on to school. Or you could take the short cut, but that meant that you'd have to cross the canal. There was no bridge, only some fairly large, stable rocks to step on. That first morning I had taken too long getting ready, so of course I had to take the short cut. All decked out in my new clothes and running along as best I could in those hard new shoes, I set out to cross the puddles, concentrating on finding the best, most sure, steppingstones. The last thing I wanted was to step in that mud. Then, out of nowhere, and totally by surprise, *whack!* someone pushed me from behind and down I went, landing smack dab face down in the gooey mud---one of the only deep mud puddles left. I peered up through the mixture of muck and tears that were quickly blurring my sight just in time to see Randy Bodell's big grin.

As I began dragging myself back home the thought came to me that this was something Randy must have planned all summer. He was waiting there the whole time. By now I was crying hard. My clothes were completely ruined. They stank! I was so upset my mom let me stay home the rest of the day.

I might have been small for my age but I had a mean streak in me like nobody's business. I vowed to get back at Randy for what he had done. Maybe he sensed it or maybe he had other things to do after school, but every day I waited for him on the way home he never came. I bet he took the long way from then on, that chicken.

Finally, after a few months had passed, and he and I had almost forgotten the whole thing, that's when I spied him leaning over the bank of the canal, apparently looking at something. This was gonna be perfect. Sneaking up, my adrenaline rising, I envisioned what would happen next. With the sound of my heart pounding in my ears, it blocked out all other sounds. This was a very intense moment in my young life.

At last I was right behind him. I put my hands out and shoved as hard as I could. Then, *Bingo!* He went headfirst into the mud. Then with my last remaining bit of wit I smirked, "So, how does it feel?"

He lunged up at me, but I had already done a 180 and was sailing on home.

Now, you'd think that every day from then on I'd trudge to and from school fearing for my life. But no, an incredible thing happened. The kids who saw me push Randy into the mud told every friend they knew, who in turn told everyone they knew, and by the time the next week rolled around I was some kind of hero at school. Maybe the story got better as it passed along, but suddenly I was perceived as a tough, brave kid. In a way it gave others the courage and strength they needed to likewise stand up to Randy. In one literal "fall" of bad luck, he had been demoted. No longer the big bad bully, he was just an ordinary kid like the rest of us.

I had learned that most of the bullies had a bark that was much worse than their bite, and that if we kids stuck together and stood up to them we could lick them.

As time passed and I met up with other bullies, it became a challenge for me to find their weakness. Although I was too small to stand up to them by myself, I could always find others to take a stand with me. For example, there was the time Richard Feckner had picked a fight with a kid much smaller and was pounding his face in. Richard was always pickin' a fight.

We were all circled around. This was one of the worst fights I had seen. There was blood everywhere, and everyone was scared for the little kid. That's when I noticed Richard's pants were starting to hang real low. He came from a family with tons of kids so he had to wear a lot of hand-me-downs. The lower they got, the more I could see what looked like girl's underwear. This was the opportunity I needed. "Look, Richard's wearing girl's underwear!" I howled.

Immediately everyone joined in the chorus: "Richard's wearing girl's underwear! Richard's wearing girl's underwear!"

Whereupon he stood up, red in the face, more from embarrassment than from fighting, tugged his pants back up, turned tail, and ran away.

Then there was the time when Danny Dale had trapped a bee in his closed fist and was chasing me with it. I was sprinting for my life when I saw an old two-by-four lying on the ground. Snatching it up, I turned and smacked his fist as hard as I could. He let out a yelp! That had to have stung in more ways than one. With the look he gave me, I feared for my life. He stood staring at me but surprisingly he turned and ran off clutching his hand.

I don't want to give the wrong impression, I never meant anyone harm. I had just come to realize that I had a low tolerance for people who enjoyed inflicting pain on other people. I simply couldn't understand it.

The very last day of school that year, I remember the feeling of total happiness that washed over me on my way home. I had passed! I had endured the rumors toward the end of the school year of how hard it was to pass the first grade. Walking home now, having passed the first grade, I was feeling pretty good about myself. I was a more mature individual for sure. *Yeah, right!*

I carried a huge cinnamon roll in my hand, which the cooks had prepared especially for our last day. And to top it off, today was my birthday.

*People who recognize life's small gifts,
the ones that are simply free for the taking,
take hold of them . . . savor them,
thus filling their lives with so much more happiness.*

3

Frogs

Far away on the other side of the world, another little girl was also preparing to face life's challenges. Although she had never heard of Sandy, Utah, or eaten cinnamon rolls, or seen fat, rough old toads, she was well acquainted with bullies.

Wynoma was just rolling out of bed. It had been another long night, tossing and turning with one of her bad headaches. Almost every night, Wynoma had headaches. Some were mild enough that if she lay real still she could drift off to sleep. But often, like last night, they were so painful she couldn't sleep at all.

The hot, humid days of summer were finally cooling off. This year it had rained more than she could ever remember. Wynoma wondered how with all that rain it could still be so hot. The rain had formed puddles. Big puddles, little puddles, puddles that were more like ponds than puddles. She had never known so much rain before. It was all quite new to her.

The hot, dry years of drought had passed, and now with the coming of the rains also came fresh garden vegetables. She imagined her mum cooking up all the good food of harvest time: steamy squash soups, fresh tomato stew, fried okra, and, of course, her favorite, corn on the cob. There was something about that fresh, sweet corn that made the old dry ground corn---the mealie maize they lived on during the dry season---seem as if the two weren't even related. She could sit down and eat ten ears all by herself she loved it so much.

Startled out of her daydream, Wynoma heard her mother calling.

"Wynoma Boneli, where are you girl? Honestly child, do I have to remind you every morning about your chores?"

Wynoma was in charge of getting her little sister and brother up and taking them down to the village well to wash up, then fetch the water for drinking and dishes, and make the long walk back in time to eat breakfast with her family. Her older brother had already gone for the breakfast water. With fifteen children in the family it took everyone working together to make things run, if they were to run at all.

Later, the older children would all go off to school, and she would be left at home with lazy Taona, little Isaac, and, of course, the two babies. Why did breakfast always seem like the whirlwinds she had seen on the plains, stirring everything up but never leaving anything good behind? With all the confusion caused by everyone starting the day off, it only made her mother more frustrated and tired than she was before. Then, like the whirlwinds, mum would not be rewarded with sweet rain, rather she felt that her scurries seemed always in vain. There didn't seem to be many rewards of motherhood.

FROGS

On her way to the well, Wynoma could see some of the early kids already heading off to school. There stood Tawanda staring and waiting to make his usual snotty remarks, "What's the matter, Wynoma, got another headache? Gonna stay home and help your mum again? I'm gonna be smart and rich and you'll still be at home mopping up the floors."

Oooooo, she hated him. Why couldn't he just keep to himself?

The real trouble was, she knew he was right. Wynoma wanted so badly to go to school, but her mum would say, "Wynoma, you'll just get one of those bad headaches, you'll lie on the ground and everyone's gonna stand there and stare. Is that what you want, girl? No, you just marry you a smart man and you'll do just fine."

On the way back to the village Wynoma got sidetracked. She could hear a little chirping sound coming from the thick bush. It didn't sound too far away, perhaps only a few meters off the worn dirt trail that led back from the well. She followed it. She told her little brother and little sister that if they would keep still, then she would give them a surprise when they got home. Wynoma was not afraid to be alone in the bush. She knew she could throw rocks and scare away most anything that lived close by. The dangerous animals like elephants and lions rarely came close to their village. It was as if they were smart enough to be afraid of man.

This sounded different than any animal she had ever heard before. Once she set a trap to catch herself a baby ape, but when the bushback zebras came wandering through the village, as they sometimes did, they smashed it to bits.

She crouched down, sneaking up ever so quietly. She didn't want to scare whatever it was. Just as she got close, the sound stopped. Wynoma knelt down and froze in place, waiting for the sound to start again.

Out of patience, and mad at herself for scaring it away, she jumped up and ran straight ahead, full force, which was just a stupid, childish thing to do, for which she got a stupid, childish reward. Wynoma fell smack dab into a muddy pond. Grabbing the nearest fern and holding on tight to pull herself out of the muck, that's when she noticed the most beautiful black, yellow, and red spotted frog. It was so tiny and cute! She held it gently between her hands and saw that it had tiny cup-like feet. She had forgotten all about her wet wrap and her muddy hair. She had found a treasure.

Hurrying back to her brother and sister she showed them the frog.

"Is this our surprise, Wynoma?"

"Yep, now we better get back."

They put it in the water bucket and scurried off to show their mum.

By now the mealie-mash maize had started to dry in the pan and on the dishes. Tembeka, Wynoma's mother, began to wonder where her children were. "Where are those children?"

Her daughter always found something to keep her mind occupied, but it wasn't always the things that would make her a good mother. Tembeka always felt sorry for her daughter Wynoma because she would not be able to attend school. But at least Tembeka would have someone to take care for her in her old age.

Wynoma came running toward their hut. She was holding the bucket in her arms instead of on her head.

"What have I told you about spilling the water? Oh, Wynoma, why do I waste my breath on you?"

"Wait, mum, look what I found. Can I keep it?"

"It's just a frog."

"I know, but I want to keep it."

"No, it'll just die. You take it right back after you do those dishes. It's all this rain that's brought them back. If you don't leave it there, then it will die, and if every child kept them, then there won't be any at all."

Wynoma just kept her little frog in a secret hiding place until the day it disappeared. She was sure she saw Tawanda snooping around just three days after she showed it to him. She should have known he couldn't be trusted.

A few weeks passed and Wynoma had forgotten all about the frog. Her mind was on bigger and better things. She had taken a head of lettuce to her trap, along with two chicken eggs, just in case apes didn't like lettuce.

The trap was made out of an old fishing net, tied to a pair of bush vines with both ends reaching into the bush. She sat still holding one end and Tawanda, trying to make up for the lost frog, sat on the other end.

Every day after school and into the evening they sat there waiting. Wynoma wanted a pet. Finally one day Tawanda said, "I'm not going; this is stupid. It's not going to work, Wynoma."

"Just this one more time, please?"

Wynoma was having a bad headache day and didn't feel like arguing with him.

"Okay, but this is it, the last time."

Tawanda hated to go. All he did was sit there. Then Wynoma would start getting cross with him, then she'd start shushing him to be quiet. It was no fun.

Today was different. As they were sitting there, a nice-sized warthog came up sniffed, and started eating the lettuce. Tawanda motioned to Wynoma to pull. She shook her head. Tawanda pulled anyway and the warthog got both feet caught in the net. Even with both feet caught it could still run, and was heading straight for Wynoma. She let out a bloodcurdling scream. Everyone within that sound came running. Tawanda, too scared to stick it out, ran too, but in the opposite direction.

Now the warthog, all tangled up in the net and just lying there frantically struggling to free himself, gave her dad quite the scare. He ran up to help Wynoma, but she had regained her composure and just pointed to the warthog and said, "I got us something for supper." They all laughed.

Back in her family's hut, Tembeka was making the final preparations for tonight's ceremony. Tonight was her family's special night. Her daughter Wynoma had been awakened from childhood into womanhood, and she wished her daughter would start acting her age or she might find that none of the village men would be interested in her.

When Wynoma and the others returned, she could see the look of disappointment in her mother's face and now she remembered why. She had hoped that if she ignored it, it would go away. She knew all the other girls looked forward to this ceremony. Why was she so different? A funeral she understood. It made sense to her that if someone died, you should dance and sing all day and night. The louder the wailing, and the more days it carried on, the more that person was loved.

But why should there be so much singing when a girl becomes a woman? She felt torn inside. She wanted to hold on to her childhood, and at the same time make some man a good wife. Would she be a good wife if she had not gone to school? Wynoma didn't want to grow up. Why, if she enjoys her life the way it is, why does it have to change?

As the biggest hut in the village began to fill up, Wynoma found herself looking around into familiar faces. She didn't understand the new feelings inside her. Uncomfortable, she began to look out at the stars in the sky. It was a clear night, no moon, and the stars seemed to be shining extra bright. As the singing started it begin to curb her uneasiness. As it got louder, she became touched, for they were singing to her. A love, a feeling of brotherhood came over her, and she felt for the first time a real part of this, her little village.

For the first time she appreciated all that her mother had taught her. She admired her mum and wished there was a way to show her. The longer the singing went on, the more she felt enlightened. Maybe there was a way she could show her mum her love and appreciation. Tembeka was a woman who believed in school. She knew this would be the only way her children could have a chance of a better life. Wynoma felt she had let her mother down because she did not go to school. Now she made a promise, to the holy ancestors and to herself, which she remembered all her life. She would make sure each of her own children would go to school, and not just primary school either, but on to learn a trade.

As sure as there is a sky above and an earth below . . . she promised.

Forget the differences, the oddities, and the flaws,
concentrate on the inside, the heart;
real joy comes---quite simply---by loving.

4

The Black and White TV

It was just an old television set, certainly one of RCA's earliest models. It was given to us by my grandmother. I can remember it, resting in the corner of her living room for what seemed like forever. It stood in an ancient upright dark-wood cabinet polished to a high sheen. Small doors on each side allowed you to close it when you weren't watching a program.

Money was tight when we were students living at the University Village, so I decided to sell our TV. I listed the old black-and-white in *The Village Line* for ten dollars, hoping to get at least five. Scott was in his second year of college at the U. of U., and I had decided not to work after our first child was born. Little Jake was now eleven months old and I was expecting a second baby. It would take all we had and more just to afford our two-bedroom apartment. We were determined to get through school without having to borrow from our parents, and at the same time, we didn't want to postpone raising a family.

A few days passed. It was one of those sweltering hot summer evenings, when a knock came at the door. I can only imagine how surprised I must have looked when I found myself face-to-face with a very tall black man. He was the tallest, blackest man I had ever seen, and I may have been the shortest, blondest lady he had ever seen. He was standing there in a dress shirt and slacks, with great beads of sweat pouring down his temples. He smiled and said, "Hello."

That smile was filled with such sincerity and warmth that it set me at ease. As soon as he greeted me in his polite, soft-spoken manner, I could tell he was just a pussycat disguised as a lion.

He said he was there to look at the TV. With those first few words I could tell he was not from America. I hoped he hadn't noticed my surprised expression at meeting him. I hadn't had a chance to meet any blacks as a child in my relatively small, predominantly white, well actually, one hundred percent white, little town. In fact, it wasn't until I was twenty, when I went back east to be a nanny, that I met and became dear friends with a very loving black couple in Connecticut. This man however, was definitely not African-American, and certainly not a person you would ever see in Utah.

I invited him in. For some reason I was very intrigued by him. I found myself wanting to ask him all sorts of questions. He patiently answered my queries in a shy sort of way. When he first spoke I could hardly understand him; his accent was so strong. But the more he talked, the more I became used to it.

Unbeknownst to me at the time, our simple conversation would open a whole new world for me.

"Where are you from?" I asked.

"Zambia."

"Where's that?"

"It is in the center of Africa."

"What are you doing here?"

"My country sent me here to obtain a master's degree."

"What are you majoring in?"

"Psychology."

"Are you here alone?"

"No, that is why I am interested in the TV. My wife came here also, but she does not work or go to school. She is very bored. That is why I need a TV."

His English was excellent, very proper, certainly much more proper than my own, which I guess isn't too surprising since I had been raised in what was then considered a hick town. But oops, wait a minute. Silly me! Why hadn't I thought of it before? I hadn't even asked him his name. "I'm sorry, what's your name?" I apologetically asked.

He smiled a huge smile and shyly replied, "Nkosi Sianonge Manjani."

Huh? I thought. I had to ask him to pronounce it for me several times before I finally got it down. Na-ko-see, Man-jan-ee.

"Would your wife like to have a visitor?" I asked.

"Oh yes, she would enjoy that very much," he responded, "her name is Tansy."

He left with the TV, paying the full ten dollars for it. When the door closed, my mind was in a blur. Africa. I knew so little about Africa. Actually the only image that came to my mind was the Hollywood version of Africa I had seen on the Tarzan movies. I loved the Tarzan movies. Oh yes, once in the third grade I gave a report on Nigeria, I think it was Nigeria. I wondered if that country was located anywhere near Zambia.

I got out the five books we owned. One happened to be my husband Scott's *World Geography* book. Lucky for me, he was minoring in geography, so we kept it. Most textbooks we sold back to the bookstore.

Africa, the largest continent next to Asia, yet it contains only a tenth of the world's total population. I read into the night, everything I could find on Africa. By the time I went to bed, the new-and-improved vision I had of Africa created images in my mind. As I drifted off, I started dreaming of the jungles, the sunsets reflecting off the water holes and framing the silhouettes of the towering Baobab trees. From my dreamy perch I could see Tansy dressed in brightly colored woven cloth wrapped around her body. She was balancing a stack of dishes on top her head, then carefully she begin to stride down with ease to the watering hole where she would immediately be surrounded by monkeys, elephants, and herds of water buffalo. Tansy, sweeping the floor of her grass hut. Tansy, scurrying out the doorway to shoo away a wandering gazelle grazing in her vegetable garden. Rivers infested by crocodiles, thick vines dipping down into the slow-moving waters, roaring waterfalls, quiet mornings at the watering hole where a mother giraffe and her lanky baby come to steal a drink. Hippos, zebras, apes, baboons, they were all there.

By morning, I was so excited that when I finally knocked on Tansy's door I was certain my overwhelming eagerness to visit with her would frighten her away.

When she answered the door, I was actually a little disappointed. She was not dressed in a colorful wraparound, rather she was wearing just a normal skirt and blouse. She was not as dark as Nkosi, and her hair was cropped short. Her features were not particularly striking nor beautiful. It wasn't until I got to know her better that I was able to see her true beauty.

Tansy, like her husband, was quiet and modest at first. She seemed to keep to herself. I wondered if she wished I would just go away, but didn't know politely how to get rid of me. We awkwardly fumbled around for something to say. Then it came to me. I invited her to accompany Jake and me over to the playground. I found out later that she was completely taken off guard by a white person being so friendly. She was shocked. In her country this would be unthinkable. So, after a few moments, she finally agreed.

The more we visited the more she opened up, and the more I discovered what a wonderful person she was. She had the cutest accent and the most contagious laugh. She giggled all the time.

I had never thought of myself as being gifted with humor. I didn't think I was funny at all. In fact I could never remember any jokes, and I hardly ever find myself laughing right out loud. But Tansy was sure laughing right out loud. She thought everything I said was funny.

As fun as Tansy was, it was her wisdom that impressed me the most. Blessed with a keen analytical mind, she was a true deep thinker. She was caring and sensitive, qualities that to this day still unite our friendship.

We talked all that day, and just about every day, for the rest of that year. It seems we were always struggling to figure out and solve the world's problems. The same things that had always angered and discouraged me were the same things that angered and discouraged her. The same things that disgusted and saddened me likewise saddened and disgusted her. For example: children being taught to hate, whether it be against race, color, or religion, was something we just couldn't understand.

We were soulmates in a joint philosophical fight against prejudices of all kinds, poverty, and the ever-widening divisions between rich and poor. Unlike me, however, she had witnessed all these things firsthand. Surprisingly, though, Tansy had not become hardened. She refused to judge, recognizing that each person is in a unique situation and that it's up to each individual to determine for himself how to make a positive difference in the world.

One of Tansy's heartiest laughs was reserved for the time I asked her whether she'd had any close run-ins with elephants or rhinos.

"Peggy, you silly girl," she scolded in jest, "I don't have those animals just walking around. I am civilized. I don't live in the bush. I live in a town. The city closest to me is Lusaka, which is probably the same size as Salt Lake City."

Tansy's patient teachings on the reality of Africa continued. I really had her going.

"My mother---her name is Wynoma---grew up in the bush. Life is so hard in the bush. You must have the rains to grow your food. If the rains don't come, you don't have food, and then you starve. If you don't end up starving then most likely something else will get you. The wild animals are always breaking down your gardens, even coming into your homes. There are no fences to keep them out. There are the bush fires and the diseases. So many people die of malaria, and there is nothing you can do for them. There are no medicines, no vitamins, no doctors. Searching for water can take days if your water hole goes bad. You must carry everything, even water, either on your head or on your back. In the bush there are no cars and no electricity.

"My mother had had enough. She wanted a better way for her children than what she had had. She heard rumors that life in the city was good and easy, so she left the bush, only to find that life was just as hard in a town when there are no jobs and you have no education. And in Lusaka, there were no jobs for my mother or my father. For a long time they wondered if this poverty was better than that which they had suffered in the bush. But my mother was a determined lady, so they stayed. Many times the women are stronger-willed than the men. The man, with his desire to provide for his family, becomes very discouraged.

"My father finally got a job with the tribal council and we lived in a one-room little home. Here's where I grew up. And to this day my mother has never slept in a real bed, only on a mat on the floor. There wasn't enough room for everyone to have a bed, so at night we rolled out a hand-woven mat. Then as we got more money to buy what we called beds they always went to the children.

"In our family there were three boys and five girls. Mother had been in the city long enough to know that jobs for girls were scarce. Maybe that's why she was so persistent when it came to school. If she caught us sneaking out of school, we really got it. She demanded that even each of her girls learn a trade. That was even after we'd finished primary school. She spent what little money she had on our education, which left none for herself. It wasn't until a few years ago when I said, "I refuse to go to school," that I found out about my mum's promise to her mother. The women in my family seem stronger than the men, not physically, but with a more clear vision. I've heard it called intuition. Whatever it was, my mum had it. Yet she could only make us half of who we are, the other half came from my father."

With each new thing Tansy told me about her mother I began to develop a genuine fondness and a great respect for Wynoma. She seemed like such a wise woman. And I only had to watch Tansy's expression when she talked about her mother to know how much she loved her. There existed a tender kinship that most of us only dream of. Because her mother was the stern one and her father was the soft, easygoing one, it wasn't until Tansy got older that she fully appreciated her mother. Her mum always made each of her children be their best, and father simply said, you do what your mother says. I began to see that Tansy was a true reflection of her mother.

Neither one of us had a car. Our only car Scott needed most of the time. So we walked anywhere and everywhere we needed to go. Tansy made the sometimes monotonous days fun. Even the most tedious tasks became interesting. Using her foreign customs she would show me how to make the tiniest tasks easier. Things like folding sheets, mopping the floor, and even how to carry things. She would say, as she watched me try to maneuver holding Jake at the same time as washing the dishes:

"Looks like you need your hands free. That's why in Africa the women carry their children on their backs. Let me show you. Find me an old sheet. Now roll it like this. Fold it here. Then tuck this up and under and, ta da! now Jack is on your back, and your arms are free."

Then she stood back to look at me and I looked at her and we both burst out laughing. I don't think I had the right build for these African wraps.

Tansy was so good at all the household chores. In Africa every child must get up and do their chores before they go to school. The only thing that I could do better than her was cook. In her country all they had to eat was what they could grow, be it vegetable or animal. She had never seen so many choices of food. She was fascinated with the combinations I could come up with, and I was certainly only an average cook. She loved watching those cooking shows on TV; in fact she loved everything on TV.

Late one night, it must have been about two or three in the morning, I was up feeding our new baby girl, Jenny. I happened to look out across the apartment building and I saw Tansy's television light still on. A few days later she told me she was discouraged because there was only one TV station that stayed on late at night.

Tansy was so much like a little child seeing things for the first time, yet some of her virtues few children, if any,

38

possess. Because I was used to a faster pace of life, I was always impressed with her patience. Maybe that's a lost virtue with us Americans. She didn't mind doing the minutest of jobs, jobs that I didn't have time for. One day, while I prepared something for dinner, she sat and organized my sewing box. Truly I am one of the most unorganized people in the world. The proof was in that box. She even untangled each strand of thread, taking care not to break a single strand. She really felt like she had accomplished something when she was done, and she had: the impossible!

I wanted Tansy and Nkosi to see how we spent our holidays, so I invited them over to my parents' house for Thanksgiving. Everyone was a little uneasy because of my new friends, but basically things ran pretty much as they always do. We got there early, we starved ourselves, or we thought we were starving. Then we all tried to make clever conversations, and last of all we stuffed ourselves. That might be a bit negative. But after listening to Tansy in the car on our way home tell of one of their holidays, that's about the way it seemed to me. All of her family love making music, singing together, dancing, and drinking African beer. They live it up, enjoy life, no matter how old they are.

I noticed the same thing when I spent two weeks in a poor little town in central Mexico. I wondered if this merry-making had more to do with not having anything else as far as material possessions, so you were forced into entertainment using your own voices and a few hand-made instruments. Or could it be because your heart remains happy, free from the bondage of wanting and acquiring things? Who can say? Yet these people were some of the happiest people I had ever met.

Three days after Christmas we had one of the biggest snowfalls I can remember. It was crazy. Tansy had never seen snow before. We all ran out and became kids for a day. We rolled the snow into huge, giant snowballs. They were so big that my six-foot-two-inch husband couldn't see over them. Then we brought out chairs and stacked them up in order to put the heads on these giant snowmen we had created. Our apartments were situated in and among rolling hills, so we got together whatever slick coats we had and began sliding down the hills, holding hands and making big trains. It was just the kind of time all those stressed-out students needed.

By now I felt as comfortable with Tansy as I did with any of my closest friends. It's funny, but after that first meeting it didn't even cross my mind that she was black. I mean, we both knew the obvious, but we felt that we were the same. Sometimes she would tell a joke like; "Being white is better than being black, right? Then how come the beaches are loaded with white people trying to get as black as they can?"

We would both laugh, but never meaning to offend each other.

Once, I remember when the fact that Tansy was black consciously registered in my mind, and it almost took me by surprise. We were invited to dinner by some close friends. "We're just having a little get-together, so you and Scott come and bring those black friends of yours."

If she had said, "Bring Nkosi and Tansy," I wouldn't have been so surprised, but it was the way she said "those black friends of yours" that really stunned me. It was as if she had to bring the obvious to my attention. Oh yeah, they are black, aren't they?

It was that little get-together that made me sad and frustrated. My friends acted so different, so uneasy, I felt as if I had to apologize to Tansy and Nkosi. The feeling in the air was so awkward that even Tansy and Nkosi couldn't be themselves. Now neither of my friends will ever really know each other.

I kept thinking, why does the color of skin have to make such a big difference? Why? I so badly wanted Tansy to be treated the same as everyone else. Isn't it what's on the inside that counts? And from what I'd seen in Tansy, and from all she'd taught me, peoples hearts were pretty much the same.

And what of Nkosi? Still the most sincere, humble, and genuine man, you'll ever find. Who couldn't love that big, yet gentle, teddy bear? It just didn't seem fair.

True, life has its ups and downs. That last winter of school had to be without a doubt the lowest point in my life.

We hoped the move would help us out financially. Scott had lost his good job and found another at much reduced pay. I was expecting our third baby. We had no insurance and literally no money. My mother had bought a one-hundred-year-old home. No one had lived in it for twenty years, and she was willing to let us stay in it rent-free.

When I explained it to Tansy, she knew we had to make that move to Redondo Avenue, twelve miles away. When she and Nkosi helped us move, neither one of us really knew that twelve miles was quite a bit farther than just next door. And the close friendship we had taken for granted would now be tested. "Yes, okay. I promise to come visit."

As the snow began to fly, we tried to heat that big old drafty house with just a wood stove. Scott was stressed trying to keep up good grades and working all sorts of extra jobs just to keep food on the table. The children all got sick, even the new baby, and we couldn't afford a doctor. They just wanted to be held. So I held them. We had no television, no radio, and to read a book was out of the question. Just as I'd get one child settled down, another would want to be held. So there I sat day after day staring at the walls and wishing I had someone to talk to.

As I sat there one day looking out the window for some sort of entertainment, I saw a woman go out and get in her car. I can still remember the feeling of envy I had for her. I envied her freedom, her touch with the outside world. I felt as if I was alone inside this big empty house and the world outside was revolving around without me.

When the days turned into weeks and still no change, my despair mounted, until one day I heard a knock at the door, then a familiar chirp. It was Tansy. She had ridden the bus down from the Village. Never do I remember being so happy to see someone.

She came in and started telling me all about her new job. She looked so happy. She said, "Let's pack up the children and ride the bus to the movies."

Even that bus ride was an adventure, with two toddlers and a baby. I was impressed once again with Tansy's patience. Jake and Jenny had never been to a movie before. They were spellbound. Jake, "Jack," as Tansy called him just to tease me, sat on Tansy's lap. She had bought the children candy and popcorn, but they were too glued to the screen to even eat. Tansy laughed so loud at all of Cinderella's little mice friends I thought the owners might ask her to leave. This was something the children needed as much as I did. When that day did come to an end I hated to see her go. She had been my friend in the good times and she did not forget me in the bad.

With the coming of spring that year, many changes were in the air. Scott graduated with honors, got the job he wanted, and we located close to where we had bought some land when we were first married. We had dreams of building our first home there soon. Nkosi had been scheduled to finish up his schooling in the United Kingdom, after which they would be heading back to their home in Zambia.

With so much to look forward to, we kept the inevitable unspoken. In surprisingly good spirits, Tansy and Nkosi helped us make our move to a little duplex two hours away. This is when I saw Tansy's real roots of strength come shining through. The more you have been hurt, the easier it is to just push your feelings down deep inside somewhere and lock them away, keeping them safe from hurt again. The African people are very good at this. I was determined to show only as much emotion as she did.

So, after we finished unpacking, we stood by their old station wagon and I gave Tansy a paper with my address on it. She tried to joke, but nobody laughed. Scott and Nkosi shook hands. Tansy and I hugged. But there were no words. What do you say when you know it's the last time you'll ever see someone you love so much? We were all quiet, very quiet. As their car pulled out of the driveway, I could barely see through my tears, but as I looked up I was just in time to catch a glimpse of Tansy. She was crying too.

Maybe you'll accomplish your goal, your aim,
maybe you won't;
but the seed is in the trying;
thankful are we to the man who plants the seeds.

5

Letters

I remember waiting for the first letter. It was a strange feeling knowing that with an ever so slight twist of fate you could lose all contact.

Now I knew just how far away Africa was. It took a month to get a letter, three months to get a package. When the first letter came I found out how much Tansy hated writing letters. My letters would be novels and hers would be short and to the point.

They stayed in the U.K. for a few years and then moved back to Zambia. Unfortunately, I can't give a very detailed account of where they went or who they knew; I had to figure everything out with some really scant letters.

There was never anything in the media giving me current events on Zambia. I don't think the internet had even been thought of yet.

It was fun getting different stamps from different places, but they could never have known the real impact this little family had on my family. Tansy had given birth to a baby girl in the U.K. She named her Tembeka, after her grandmother and the baby's great-grandmother. Then, about five years later, her baby boy Simba was born.

Trying to make a living in Zambia was very hard, maybe even harder on Nkosi and Tansy because they had experienced the material life we Americans know. Zambia had gone from being a dictatorship form of government when Nkosi and Tansy used to live there, to a form of democracy when they got back. But with freedom came the price each country has had to pay for it. Inexperience, lack of education, coupled with trying to unite all the people, makes it all so difficult. Next, a country needs exports and relies on them. Zambia had few of its own exports. All these problems combined made the Zambian dollar fall from one and a quarter times the value of the American dollar to four hundred times lower in only ten years. This is why Nkosi and Tansy were able to come to the U.S. back then, but now it would be impossible.

Once, when things got real bad in Zambia, I wrote and asked, what can I do to help? Perhaps I could send something, would that help? Her mother needed shoes, her family needed clothes. Yes, I could send those items, but how could I send money?

We came up with a plan. First I sent some packages just to see if Tansy would get them. She did. Now came the hard part. I knew the people at the post office in Africa may go through the packages and take what they want. Also, it was difficult to communicate since letters took a month going either direction.

I took a cardboard box and cut a hole in the middle in the shape of a square. Then I peeled back one layer of paper from the square, exposing an inner layer of swirly paper. Carefully I took out the swirly paper and forced a one hundred dollar bill up into the swirls, then pasted all the layers back together. Then I wrote a letter to Tansy that I knew would get there before the package, explaining what she should do when she got the package. I wrote, "Very carefully tear all of the cardboard apart."

It worked! She got the money.

Tansy's mother with her thankful heart sent me three doilies, which she had crocheted herself. Quite a sacrifice to come up with the money just to send them, I was sure. Tansy's country, that she loved so much, was falling apart. No one can understand poverty like this unless they have seen it with their own eyes. Even the Christian Children's Fund started going there to help the starving children.

Tansy said that through it all her mother could never turn anyone away. It didn't matter even if it was a stray dog, she felt compassion for them. She had very little means herself, but she gave what she had. Things got so bad; the poverty level rose and jobs became scarce.

Nkosi and Tansy felt they had no choice but to leave their dear homeland. This was no place to raise children. Nkosi applied for a position at any university in South Africa, which was a first world country and, from what they had heard, very industrialized. Since it was only two countries away from theirs, they figured they could drive home whenever they wanted to.

Nkosi got a job at the University of Port Elizabeth in Port Elizabeth, South Africa.

Now started our interest in South Africa. They had problems of their own. The white minority government wanted to force the native black people to live in what they called "townships." The whites (five million) had total control over the blacks (thirty million). The whites owned all the factories, all the capital, all the gold and diamond mines, and even all the farmland.

Tansy and Nkosi, because they were black, were forced to live in one of the townships. These townships all had different levels of poverty. Some didn't have drinking water or proper sewers, and many had no electricity.

As the blacks became more educated their self-esteem began to rise. They no longer wanted to be told what to do, and some started to rebel.

Tansy said that at Nkosi's university she heard of some black boys wanting to listen to Pink Floyd, a popular band in America. Since the white apartheid leaders didn't want their blacks to get any ideas from the Americans, they came in their room and shot them all dead. I was real scared for Tansy and her family. Back here at home we read anything we could find about South Africa, because that's where our friends were. I didn't know that as long as you were passive and conforming there was no threat on your life.

A friend of ours told us about a video he had heard of. He said it was a true story of a white journalist in South Africa. It was called "Cry Freedom." We immediately found it and watched it. We couldn't believe what we saw.

A white man, seeing the inhumane torture the white apartheid government officials were inflicting on the black people, wanted to help. He was able to develop a warm friendship with an outspoken, caring black man who just wanted everyone to be treated equally. Frustrations mounted among the white government, himself, and his black friends. The white government murdered, by beating to death, his close black friend, Steven Biko. Now he, Donald Woods, was a voice speaking out against the injustices.

I was sickened. The more I watched, the more I wondered how any one group of people could treat another group of people as if they weren't people at all.

I guess after watching American blacks come so far I thought we had become feeling human beings, willing and wanting to treat all men as equals. It had taken a long time to come that far but we had made great progress. There were enough people who knew the Ku Klux Klan was evil. There were enough of us who weren't prejudiced, and we outnumbered the sick-minded people who were so proud they could physically abuse, mentally torment, and find pleasure in watching others suffer. Hadn't we as a people risen above that?

Well, apparently not in South Africa. At this time the whites equaled about seventeen percent of the total population and yet they ruled over the rest. They did not rule with kindness, understanding, and fairness. No, the only way they could have possibly had control over so many people was to take away their dignity, their feelings of self-worth, humiliate them, and rule by fear. If one can convince another that they are of no value, of no need, and of no self-worth, then they can have complete rule. You just have to make sure you stay in control. You must make sure the other people never have a chance to feel needed and never have a chance to be educated.

Then, if by some unforeseen flaw in the system one or two want what you have, then you must secretly or in the open gun them down. That will create enough fear to keep the rest of them where you want them. Shut them down with force. No, this does not happen now, not these days, we are above all that, aren't we?

We were so taken by this new knowledge that we wanted to do something. But what could we do? It was the age-old obstacle of what one person can do against an entire force. We would start by showing that we cared about those black people, and that we wanted justice for them.

One Sunday, Scott heard about a revival at a Lutheran church in Park City. Just like hundreds of little communities all across America who now had knowledge of what was going on, we rallied together for the blacks. Denominations of all kinds came together to pray for them. When you are united in a common cause you forget about your differences. You pull together. I know in our car alone we had two Lutherans, a Baptist, an agnostic, and a Latter-day Saint, all feeling the need to help. Nothing else mattered. It was right battling wrong and we wanted to represent right.

Since we had moved to Heber City we lived only about thirty minutes from Park City. Here came the carload from Heber City pulling into Park City's Catholic church, donated for the Lutherans to use since they were expecting such a large crowd. We were all busy talking about South Africa.

To this day I wonder if the blacks had any idea we were all pulling for them. I have always believed that there are more good-hearted people in this world than evil people, and I have yet to change my mind. Sometimes we just need to get over our differences, stop worrying about ourselves so much, and reach out.

We came away wishing we could have done more. It would take many more years and unfortunately many more deaths before the blacks would be able to see the light at the end of the tunnel. Finally, in 1994 when the animosity was at a peak and the white government feared a civil war by the blacks threatening an uprising, they agreed for the first time in this country's history to allow blacks the freedom to vote. They elected the first ever black president, Nelson Mandela, by a majority vote. We could only imagine the pressure on this man. How could one man turn around an entire nation that was filled with so much hate?

I want to share a little incident that happened in this Lutheran church. I tell it only to show the innocence of a child and to make the point that if a child is not raised with hatred, intolerance, or petty hang-ups they can feel comfortable anywhere.

I rode to the church the first week with some very good friends. I enjoyed it so much that I wanted to take my family the next week. Scott and I packed up all five kids and headed off to a church my children had never even heard of.

First, we prayed for the unrest in South Africa. Then the pastor asked the children who had practiced their African song to come up front and sing it for the congregation. We were in a state of shock when our youngest daughter got up, marched right down to the front and turned around to face every unfamiliar face in that congregation. She didn't show an ounce of fear. Then, just as if she had rehearsed the song, she proceeded to sing like she knew it. My older children, now more wise and mature, were totally embarrassed for her---or was it for themselves?

Although they were uncomfortable, she never flinched; the smile on her beaming face just got bigger and bigger.

Even if the blacks were better qualified they were never paid as much as the whites in South Africa. The Manjanis were no exception. Since Nkosi was educated he had a job that was better than most blacks. They didn't stay in the poorest township long. They were able to move up to the point where they even could afford a phone for a short while. What a shock when Tansy called me one day. It sounded like she was right in my backyard.

It's funny how you have certain friends with whom you pick up right where you left off, even if you haven't seen them for years. Tansy was one of those friends. I told her not to worry about the phone bill because I would help her pay it. We talked for a whole hour, but it seemed like it was too short. Our children were getting older so I guess that meant we were older too. But I didn't feel any older, and she didn't sound any older.

She teased me by asking, "How is "Jack" and Jenny? And how is your garden growing?"

We had moved several times since the last time I saw her, but she knew me well enough to know I wouldn't live anywhere without a garden. This gave me the perfect opportunity for a comeback, "How long did it take you to kill yours?"

It was great. She had the worst luck when it came to gardening.

Although school teaching is not a high-paying job, Scott was also a licensed contractor who spent his summers building homes. In fact, he had built three for us, two of which we sold and made enough money to nearly own our third. This was only possible because our homes didn't keep getting bigger.

With the children nearly grown, I had time to work on my passion: growing things. We had never had any extra money for flowers because the children and the home took all we had, so the flowers that I had were all given to me. Now we were reaching a point in our lives where we had a little extra money, so Scott and I spent some on ourselves. I promptly bought up flowers---all different kinds of flowers. I had a neighbor say to me, "Peg, if you like flowers so much you should get a job at that nursery down the road. All they sell is flowers."

I went down and, guess what?---I got the job! I was so excited. It would be my first job since starting my family, and I would be working with something I love: flowers. The nursery did not pay nearly enough for me to be able to save much money, but it gave me the knowledge I needed to start a business of my own. Because of my flower business, I started to save for a trip to Africa. I bought the very cheapest laundry soap, dish soap, and shampoo. I bought all my clothes at the secondhand stores. We drove old cars, but, hey, they were paid for, and I saved, saved, saved.

Tansy and I had corresponded for twenty years now. Finally, one Christmas I announced to my kids, next Christmas I am going to Africa. Well, to kids a year seems like a long time; to me it was forever.

I wrote to Tansy informing her of my plans. Nkosi had got a new job at the University of the Western Cape in Cape Town, South Africa. This put them even farther away from their home, but with the pay increase they would be able to afford a place outside of the townships.

I worked hard that year getting enough money together for my anticipated trip. When I got talking with a travel agent, she said it would take two days just to get to Cape Town. Then I wanted to travel up to Zambia with Tansy to meet her mum and family, which would be another four days by car. It seemed I would need at least a month to see all I wanted to, and even at that it would be cutting it close. I wondered how this news would go over with my family.

Let's see, what could I cut out? Nkosi had always said that if I ever came he would take me to see Victoria Falls, one of the seven wonders of the world. I wanted to meet---no, I *had* to meet Tansy's family, especially her mother, Wynoma. I had to see the universities, the animals, the jungles. I had to spend time, lots of time, with my dear friends. I couldn't cut anything out. So I broke the news to my family. The kids were a little hesitant, but after my map-loving husband got looking at my destinations, he said, "You take as long as you need, this is a once-in-a-lifetime trip!" Oh, I could have squeezed him till he popped!

My excitement was building with every letter. Tansy said that if I came I should come in their summer, which was our winter. Perfect! The kids would all be in school and I certainly don't plant flowers in January. I could be gone all winter. But I didn't think my family would go for that. So I planned to go right after Christmas and stay as long as I needed.

Now I worked on getting my passport, visas (both kinds), shots (yuck), and, of course, luggage. I bought the biggest two suitcases I could find. I filled them up with all kinds of trinkets and Juicy Fruit gum to give to the kids, clothes to give to the adults, and gifts for my friends. I had insect repellent for the mosquitoes, lots of disinfectant soaps and lotions, notebooks and pens, everything I thought I may need in a Third World country, even the best water purifier money could buy. I had thought of everything. Or had I?

Tansy had written me a letter and said they were making preparations for my arrival. She had swept the dirt floor so I would have a place to sleep. Oh, that Tansy, she loves to tease; or, well, I think she's teasing.

There are two absolutes in each person's life;
one is birth, the other is death.

6

My Turn in Africa

The night before I was to leave there was a special program on television showing the violence in Johannesburg, South Africa. There were media accounts of people living in fear, locking their doors with seven different locks, not going out after dark, and hurrying from their homes to their cars and from their cars to their homes. It was said that all this was happening to the whites. So the whites tired of living in fear were fleeing for their lives.

My children turned it on and as soon as they mentioned the words "South Africa," my kids said, "Hey look, Mom, that's where you're going."

That's when the phone calls started. First was my mom.

"Have you seen this thing on TV? I just don't think you should go."

I tried to reassure her by telling her I was not going to Johannesburg, I was going to Cape Town. She calmed down a bit, and simply said, "Just be careful. I'm so worried about you."

No sooner had I hung up the phone than my mother-in-law called.

"I've been watching this thing on TV. I don't want you to go. I don't care how much those airplane tickets cost you. Please, Peg, we love you, don't go."

By now my own family began to worry. I tried to think of things to tell them that would make them feel better.

"Oh, you know the media, everything is always blown out of proportion. They are always trying to get people to watch so they will use anything they can think of to get your attention. They will even use shock value, scare tactics. Don't you see? They are only trying to make a story. I'm so tired of seeing only the bad. Why can't they ever show the good? Now listen, my friends live there, don't they? If they thought it was dangerous they would have told me, right?"

I didn't want them to know it, but I was a bit nervous because I hadn't heard from my friends for a final confirmation, and they didn't have a phone. But, as my husband said to a friend, "You know Peg, once she makes up her mind to do something she does it."

I just kept on packing. I was set on going, no matter what. That's when a dear friend, Bonnie, called. She didn't know it at the time but she was an answer to a prayer. She had somebody from her work going to Cape Town. If my friends didn't show up at the airport I could call their hotel. Yes! The final obstacle hurdled. At least I had a back-up.

In the morning I was on a plane heading to Dallas-Fort Worth, then on to Miami, and then on to Cape Town.

My experiences with flying you could count on one hand. So, when changing flights went really smooth for me, I was relieved. Actually I was so excited, I never remember being scared.

Once on the South African Airways plane, that's when my world as I knew it began to be somewhere in the past. For the truly international fliers this might sound silly, but I felt like a little country girl finally coming out into the big world.

Right next to me sat two children, both speaking Afrikaans. Directly to the side of me was a group of about six black students, all with British accents, and in front of me was a man currently living in L.A., but originally from South Africa.

Accents changed, the food changed, even the flight attendants were from South Africa. I think the family sitting next to me from Johannesburg painted a most accurate picture of South Africa.

I started a conversation with the children. "Do you speak English?"

"Yes, a little," they answered with a strong accent. They were wearing T-shirts from Disney World so I figured they had been vacationing there. Pretty smart, huh?

"So, how did you like America? How did you like Disney World?"

"Oh, we love it!" the little brother piped up, "it's so clean."

His sister elbowed him and said, "Don't talk so loud."

He ended up being quite a bit less reserved than his sister.

"I like your accent."

In unison, "We like yours."

Then the sister, starting to warm up a bit, said, "You are from America. I wish I talked like you. We want to live in America some day."

Now having my first audience I couldn't wait to show them my pictures I had brought from home. "Would you like to see some pictures of where I live?"

"Yes, we'd love to!"

I got in my carry-on bag and took out the little silk pouch of pictures. I had chosen some of my favorites, many of which were of my flower gardens. As I began to tell them stories of each one, I was surprised how wonderful they thought they were. I knew they were nice, but not that nice.

"They are so-o-o-o nice, not like South Africa."

"Oh, why's that?"

As I started to put my pictures away, I was startled by their next few comments.

"It is very dirty where we live," little brother piped in.

"Dirty?"

"Yeah, trashy because of the blacks."

Now his sister got real annoyed; there were blacks sitting all around us.

"Can't you talk a little more quiet?"

She saw that I was not at all shocked, nor surprised, by his statements. So they began to share all of their feelings about their country.

"The blacks are ruining our country. They sleep in the streets, they throw their papers everywhere. They are even taking over our government. Now there is getting to be so many of them that they are even taking over our jobs. When we go on an American airplane we have white stewardesses, but when we fly on South African Airways we have black stewardesses."

When they asked me where I was going, obviously I didn't tell them my friends in Cape Town were black.

"To stay with a friend in Cape Town."

"Oh, you're lucky. Cape Town isn't so bad, but it's getting there."

After the next incident, I was no longer surprised that these children could be so prejudiced. The flight attendants had been around to ask everyone what they wanted for dinner. I could hear a considerable amount of commotion directly behind me. A man was yelling at a black attendant. It went on for such a long time that people all around me began to get uneasy. My new little friend sitting next to me said, "Oh, that's my stepfather, he's got quite a temper."

Still the commotion went on. Then she tipped her head down and said, "I'm so embarrassed."

I was straining my ears to hear what the man was saying. It was something like this, "But you deliberately skipped over me . . . I've noticed . . . ever since we started this flight you have been smug with everyone . . . I don't like your attitude."

By this time the poor girl was in tears and he demanded to see her boss. She turned and walked down the aisle. When she returned a black man was walking behind her. I couldn't help smiling to myself. The manager apologized up and down for the girl.

Then the man proceeded to get angry with the whole airplane. Nobody got the attention they deserved. According to him, it was all because "You people are ruining South African Airways, just like you're ruining our country."

There was a black lady sitting next to him. She got up and went back to visit with the flight attendants and never returned to her seat. Now, I guess I could be wrong, but after watching this family all night even the man's wife seemed scared of him.

The flight lasted about twenty hours. I left Miami at 5:00 P.M. and arrived in Cape Town at 1:00 P.M. the next day. After having supper, breakfast, and lunch on the plane, we finally landed at the Cape Town Airport. The children and I exchanged addresses and wished good luck to each other, then I got off, and my little friends stayed on to take their remaining three hour-flight home.

The South African airport was smaller than I had expected. We had to walk down the stairs from that huge 747 and outside across the runway and into a small building. And here I was worried about whether I would be able to find Tansy or not, and there were only a dozen people in the first room, maybe thirty people in the next one.

With only one flight every other day from America, it would be pretty hard for anyone to miss you. There was only one luggage pickup, so I had no trouble finding my luggage.

I was trying not to let myself get too excited but my stomach was a whirl of butterflies. I turned around to start seriously searching the people and at that moment I saw Nkosi. I had been so worried I wouldn't recognize the Manjanis after twenty years. Nkosi looked exactly the same. I couldn't believe it. It must have been that familiar smile.

Just then I heard a little voice say, "There she is, Dad."

Nkosi had carried an old worn and faded photo of me, yet the children had studied it, which enabled them to be in on the hunt too!

We were all a bit clumsy at first. I didn't know whether to hug Nkosi and he didn't know whether to hug me. So we both fumbled around with the luggage instead and then, trying to inconspicuously wipe tears from our eyes, we proceeded to ask each other questions.

"So, how was your flight?"

"Very nice, they fed me so much I think I must have gained ten pounds on just three flights."

Everyone laughed.

"Where is Tansy?"

"She had to work."

"Oh, I didn't know Tansy had a job."

"She just got it a few weeks ago."

"I'm so glad you were here. I was so worried, wondering if anyone would be here to pick me up. So this must be Simba and this must be Tembeka. You are both so quiet. Why aren't you in school?"

Simba blurted out, "It's summer vacation!"

They were both staring at me, as if they had heard all about me and were trying to figure out if any of it was true. The children were being very shy and that was good because I had so many questions filling my brain that I couldn't shut up. I was asking Nkosi one hundred and one questions all at once. He, with his quiet, calm nature tried to answer them all or wisely said, "There will be time for that."

When I went to get in the car they all started laughing. It was as if they were planning a joke and it just happened. I couldn't figure it out.

"What is so funny?"

I stood waiting by what I thought was the passenger side of the car. Then Nkosi said, "Are you driving?"

They all started laughing again. I can't count how many times they caught me on that joke during my stay in South Africa where they drive on the opposite side of the street, and sit on the opposite side of the car.

The first thing I noticed when we left the airport was the trash; there was paper everywhere. Maybe I noticed because of what the children on the plane had said, but it just looked dirty. Now I knew what they had meant.

There were fences everywhere with papers trapped against them by the wind. Across the fences I got my first glimpse of a township. I knew what it was without even asking. I had read about them, and it looked every bit as awful as I had imagined.

We drove past Nkosi's university. There were black people everywhere, walking, lying on the sidewalks, and selling things in the middle of the streets. There was a minivan kind of thing honking behind us. It was crammed full of about twenty-five black people---and I mean full. Nkosi informed me on that first day that when one of these vans gets behind you, you move out of the way. They don't stop for anything and they wouldn't hesitate to sideswipe you. Every time I saw them after that I noticed that they were banged up. Only black people rode in them. They were like taxis only, carrying so many people, they were all on a tight schedule to be on time.

Nkosi tried to explain the way it was here. "You've got the white people like you," pointing at me. These were mostly Dutch immigrant settlers. "You've got the black people like me," pointing to himself, meaning native blacks originating in the African countries. "And you've got a mixture of the two, which they refer to as coloreds, in between you and me. Most coloreds don't like being called colored, but it is the only way to know which people you are talking about."

The ride home was dominated by my questions so Simba and Tembeka didn't say a word all the way home. I used to wonder what the children would call me. I had decided that I would really like it if they called me Aunt Peggy, but since I wasn't black maybe I couldn't be considered an aunt. What a funny thing because the very first thing I heard Nkosi call me was Auntee Peggy. So, that was that. I was Auntee the rest of the time.

Simba was the first to warm up to me. Tembeka was a little more reserved. When we got to their house, they all were eager to show me around. It was so much nicer than I had imagined. In my last letter, Tansy said they lived in a flat, an apartment, with three bedrooms on the top floor so the children had to be quiet all the time. Now seeing this house was even a bigger surprise than finding out that they owned a car.

Nkosi gave me a tour of each room and said, "If you want anything from the kitchen, help yourself."

He had to go back to school for a while. It felt so strange really being there. I had just come from seeing and living in homes where people's incomes were six times what they were here. I just kept thinking I had stepped back in time forty years.

The house had four bedrooms and two bathrooms. They had appliances, a television, and even a phone, but everything was old and very used like it came from a secondhand shop. The walls were in need of a new coat of paint. The curtains looked like the ones back home that you would find at a yard sale. The yard had dead grass, but there were some struggling flowers, and even an old swimming pool.

In other words, if you tried to live off one sixth of what you make now some things would just have to wait, right?

For the next few hours while we waited for Tansy to get home, the children and I sat on the living room floor and talked. I enjoyed their company so much. They showed me what the money looked like in their country; I showed them mine. They got out a map and showed me where they used to live in Port Elizabeth and their real home in Zambia. I showed them where in the United States I was from.

We got out their old photo albums. There I was in some very old faded pictures. It was back at the University of Utah when we built those giant snowballs and made snowmen. I had completely forgotten that day. The children started laughing when I said, "Look, that's me." As Simba sat right next to me he began to snuggle closer and that made me feel good. This little boy, now nine, had only known me, a complete stranger from America, for about an hour, but I could tell already that he liked me.

It made me think about all the times when you're in a crowd and a stranger brushes up against your shoulder and you immediately pull back. Maybe he and I could be considered almost strangers but I sure liked his little black arm resting on mine. Why are most of us too busy or too set in our ways to ever let this kind of opportunity happen to us? Little Simba and I were such an unlikely pair but, strange as it seems, that made it all the more special.

Tembeka kept staring at me. She told me I looked like Meg Ryan. Yeah, right! Anyway she knew how to get on my good side. She knew all the movie stars from America. She asked which ones I had met. Just because I'm from America I'm supposed to know the stars personally. I had to explain that I was from a little town, nowhere near Hollywood, and not everyone from the States knew movie stars. I could tell they were a bit disappointed so when Simba said his favorite person was Michael Jackson, I told him I could dance just like Michael Jackson.

He selected a record from among his big old albums and small single 45s. It was a bit scratched and fuzzy but we cranked it up nice and loud and I danced for them. They actually thought I was good. My girls at home would have been so-o-o-o-o embarrassed.

Just then we heard someone at the door. "It's Mum!" Simba yelled, "turn it down!"

Then we heard Tansy unlocking all the locks, fumbling to get in. She ran to me and hugged me, and we cried, and we cried, and we stared, and we stared, and then we both burst out laughing. I don't know about her, but I had forgotten just how much I loved her.

She looked exactly the same to me, but her hair had long braids. I had never seen her hair like this before. I liked it. Then right away we picked up where we had left off. There was so much to share, I could hardly believe it was real.

Immediately, she gave me the shocking news. Her mother had died. I just kind of sat there, no reaction, listening to all the details, but not having any of them sink in. I don't know, I just couldn't get it to register in me.

Tansy tried to explain, "She was fine one day and then felt sick the next day, and then had a fever, went in to see the doctor, and he told her she had malaria. She passed away just a day later."

Still, I just sat there---no reaction. Tansy must have thought I was very rude. But I couldn't believe it. I had missed knowing her mother by one week. It just couldn't be true. For so many years I had wanted to meet this wonderful person. I remembered all the stories Tansy had told me about her. Now she was telling me more, "I didn't even have time to tell you, Peggy, it all happened so fast. Tembeka and I drove to Zambia for the services. Funerals are different here; they can last days. We just got back Sunday. I didn't want it to ruin your plans."

Then, like a light turning on, I thought for the first time, what about Tansy? She must be hurting badly.

As usual Tansy kept it all inside. She wasn't even crying. I asked her if she was okay, or if she needed some time to be alone. "No," she said, "the only thing that has kept me from feeling the hurt has been knowing that you were coming. I am too happy to be sad."

We talked and talked. We talked while she whacked apart a whole chicken. We talked while we ate dinner, which tasted like soap, and we talked after everyone had gone to bed. At last, my lack of sleep had caught up with me and I became too delirious to talk anymore, so I went to bed.

After sleeping for only a couple of hours, I awoke in the wee hours of the morning with a heavy heart. I hate to admit it, but I was feeling sorry for myself. Last night when Tansy told me about her mother, there was more to the news than just sadness. Now it began to sink in; we would have to change our whole plans. I was so disappointed. We would not be traveling to Zambia as I had wanted to do for all these years. Tansy could not miss any more work, as she was new and had yet to prove herself in her position. She had taken a job at Nkosi's rival university. He taught at the University of the Western Cape, formerly an all-black school, but recently opened to any race. Tansy got a secretarial job at the University of Cape Town, formerly an all-white school that was just starting to accept blacks. Her university had already started classes, and his would be starting in two weeks.

They were going to show me all around South Africa, but only on evenings and weekends. During the day I could see everything with the children as my guide, and they would leave me a car. I could see my whole adventure disappearing. As I lay there upset, I began to see the bigger picture.

Tansy and Nkosi had just bought this house and they just got a phone. I looked around my room. It only had one bed and one old cupboard, not even a single picture on the wall. On the cupboard was a box of chocolates placed neatly on top of a handmade doily. Next to the chocolates was a little plant all in bloom. Inside the cupboard was a new set of sheets, and I could tell I was sleeping on new sheets too. These things were all luxuries to them. They had gone all out to make sure I was comfortable. I had even asked Tansy how they could afford the house and she said, "If we end up losing it, then we lose it, but we'll go on. After all, it's just a house."

I knew they had done it all for me. They wanted things to be nice for me, and I had been thinking only of myself.

I decided right then and there to be glad just for being here. I made a promise to myself that I would appreciate all they had done for me. I became determined to be happy just to stay in Cape Town and visit with my friends.

A real calm, peaceful feeling came over me. I lay there thinking of things I would do for them. It would be fun. I could use the money I had brought for travel to buy things like dinner, movies, and so on, extra things they couldn't usually afford.

I felt the joyful feeling that comes when you give rather than receive. I fell asleep with a happy heart, knowing things would be better in the morning.

If we claim to be religious,
then why do we love some more . . .
and some less . . . and some not at all.

7

The Salvation Army Church

I'm in a deep sleep, at last. Somewhere in my dreams I hear Michael Jackson, or is it Michael Jackson? The music keeps getting louder and louder. I keep getting more and more awake, until finally I recognize the voice. It isn't Michael Jackson at all, it's Simba singing as loud as he can with the stereo turned up as loud as it will go, and he is singing along with Michael. I looked at the clock. It was only seven o'clock in the morning. Tansy told me, "Sleep in as long as you like because Simba will be the only one home tomorrow and he never gets up until you wake him up."

Obviously, not so today. He was up and wide awake. How could I be mad at him? He had thought of a way to wake me up only because he was excited to spend the day with me. I got up and said, "Okay, Simba, I'm awake. You can turn that music down now."

Tembeka had gone to register for her first year of high school. She would be gone till noon, so it was just Simba and I this morning. I made him some breakfast of French toast. He said it was his favorite. Universal food, because no matter where you go in the world you can almost always find bread and eggs.

We spent the day singing to all kinds of old music and taping African music for me to take home. When Tembeka got home I said, "Let's go shopping and surprise your mom with dinner tonight."

I had the great idea of making chicken enchiladas. Not such a universal food, as I soon found out.

It turned out that there were two everyday things that I took for granted. One was shopping and the other was driving. Nkosi had said, "I am going to ride with Tansy to work so that you can have a car."

Great, only he had forgotten one thing---okay two things---I can't drive on the opposite side of the street and I am terrible with directions.

This is what always happened: I would go to get in the car and the kids would start laughing.

"No, you get in on the other side. You are driving, remember?"

I just couldn't get used to this. Not only were you supposed to drive on the left side of the street, but everything in the car was opposite too. The steering wheel was on the opposite side, the stick shift, the wipers, and the blinkers. Indicators, as they called them. So every time I wanted to turn, I would turn on the windshield wipers, and the kids would scream with delight, "The indicators, Auntee Peggy, the indicators."

I tried hard to concentrate on staying on my side of the road, but like I told the kids, driving is something you have done for so long it's almost as if you've been on auto-pilot and now you have to learn everything all over again. I would find myself going on the wrong side of the island until I heard Tembeka scream, "The other side, Auntee, the other side!"

I would freeze up, stop, get oriented, then back up to get on the right, no, I mean, left side of the street.

My other problem was that I just couldn't get oriented. I made wrong turns all the time and Simba, my navigator, always got me back on the right street. I am surprised that I never heard the kids say they refused to ride with Auntee anymore.

Shopping turned out to be another disaster. I made a shopping list of some things I would need to make dinner for the next few days. Then when we got to the store I sent Tembeka looking for them.

Enchilada sauce . . . um . . . okay, so we'll use something else. Sour cream . . . um . . .okay, so we'll use something else. Frozen orange juice . . . um . . . okay, so we'll use something else. Cold cereal, cilantro, chili powder, on and on, only to find the same results: nothing. I think Tembeka must have been frustrated with my requests, but she never showed it.

I would say, "Have you got any tortilla chips?"

And she would say, "Do we have any what?"

All we could do was smile. I started to think she thought I was making things up.

And that's pretty much the way our shopping experience went. When we got home I served South African-style chicken enchiladas for dinner. Everyone asked, "So this is what you eat at home?"

And I answered, "Well, sort of."

Next day Nkosi said, "I think you're ready to drive by yourself today. If you drop me off at my university then you can have the car and go anywhere you like."

I knew he was only being nice but I thought, oh, joy! If he only knew how uncomfortable I was. Ah, but alas, he was drawing me a map. Now that made me feel much better, right?

"You can't go wrong," he assured me.

Yeah, okay, whatever you say. I was doing great when he was in the car, but as soon as he left I started looking at the map. I wasn't sure which direction to hold it. I couldn't figure out north and south, let alone east and west. Anyone who knows me knows that I am doing well, if, when they say, "Turn right," I turn right. I started off by going straight when I was supposed to turn right. Things began to look unfamiliar real fast.

Since the first day I got to Cape Town my friends had told me about keeping my wallet out of sight, and to never tell anyone I'm lost because as soon as I speak they will know I'm from America---and stay out of the townships. Well, right in front of me was a township. That's when I noticed the way the blacks were treated by the whites, reminding me of my original feeling that I had stepped back in time forty years, and that now I was back in the American fifties.

It's bad enough to be lost when you feel like your surroundings are safe, but when you fear everyone, it's worse. I didn't know who to trust, I didn't know who to ask, so I just kept driving around looking for this big tall building. If I saw it, I would know where I was. It was a landmark Nkosi told me to watch for.

I couldn't read any of the street names because they were all in Afrikaans, the language which had evolved from the early Dutch settlers. It was getting real hot in the car. I had just come from winter, January, freezing temperatures in Utah, to one hundred-degree summer temperatures in Cape Town. I pulled into a factory-type building and asked the uniformed guard how to get home, according to my map. He looked at the map and blurted out something in English, but his accent was so strong I couldn't understand it.

Hot, scared, alone in a town where everything was so unfamiliar, and trying to remember to keep on the left side of the road, I was feeling pretty desperate. Nkosi had given me his phone number at the university, but I didn't want him to know I had become lost. Also, I didn't want to get out of the car to look for a phone, and I'm not sure I would have known how to use it anyway.

I did what every woman does when she's lost. I kept asking until I found someone I could understand. A very nice colored man explained part of the way and a nice white South African man, whose English was harder to understand than the colored man's, told me the rest of the way. I even had to ask when I was one block from home. I came in the door shaking and said I would never drive alone again.

At about 2:30 I had no choice; I had to pick up the kids from school. Luckily, the one place I did know how to get to was Tembeka's school. Once I got there, she showed me the way to Simba's school, and then together they showed me the way to Nkosi's university.

Once we picked up Nkosi, he had a little errand to run for Tansy. The children needed a few items to make their school uniforms complete. We drove around looking for the two stores in the area that sold uniforms.

It was amazing to see so many black people walking, and not just inside the city. Because they didn't own a car, people were walking clear from the townships to anywhere that would pay them. The townships are not in the city, but the jobs are. The black taxi vans help some, but not nearly enough. People still had to walk great distances. Sometimes they have to walk so far after work that they get real tired and they fall asleep right on the sidewalks.

Today we saw a man who had fallen asleep right on the curb and his feet were hanging out into the street. Cars were swerving out around his legs, and I cringed at the thought of someone running over his legs. When I could keep it in no longer I asked Nkosi, "What was wrong with that man?"

"What man?"

"The man lying on the curb?"

"Oh, he is probably just tired; maybe he has worked all night."

"But someone could run over his legs!"

"I'm afraid we have all gotten used to seeing this. If someone is lying in the middle of the street, you just go around them. It is just a common thing to see."

That made me think back to what the children on the airplane had said about the people sleeping in the streets. At the time I thought, yeah, right! They are probably just passed out from too much drinking. Now I had seen how far these people walk, I had seen the conditions in which they live, and if you have no pride in yourself you don't care where you sleep.

Just then as we pulled into a parking lot all these men started hollering at us.

"What do they want, Nkosi?"

"The poor people have thought of everything they can do to make money. They even stand in parking lots and direct you where to park. Then when you get out they'll say, 'I'll watch your car for you.' Only they have become quite a nuisance since nobody asked them to do this anyway. I have heard that if you don't pay them, they may scratch your car."

I noticed that Nkosi always paid them, but most just ignored them. I thought to myself, Well, why wouldn't you pay them? Obviously they are much worse off than any of us who drive cars. Maybe they have no trades and maybe they never went to school, maybe their parents couldn't afford to pay the fees it takes to educate children here. Tansy told me there is no free public education available here.

As always I waited for Tansy to get home to ask her my deepest questions, the ones I had about life, hard questions. But I thought, maybe she would have some answers. She always smiled and said, "Peggy, why are you always trying to solve the world's problems?"

This time when she came home and while we were making supper, I asked a simple question, "Don't they have a minimum wage here? Yesterday a man came to your door asking for a job. I think he wanted to clean your house or something. I couldn't quite understand him. Today we saw people trying to show you where to park your car. What do these kinds of people get paid?"

"Peggy, the answers to your questions do not lie in something as simple as minimum wage."

She then tried to explain to me how things were.

"If a poor man comes to your door, he'll ask you for a job. 'Madam, I can vacuum, I can sweep, do dishes, anything.' You must reply, 'I don't need anything done.'

" 'Okay,' he'll say, 'a slice of bread? Can you spare a slice of bread?'
You must again say no.

" 'Oh, madam, a glass of water?'

"Maybe by now you start to feel sorry for him, so you give him a glass of water. The next day he comes again. This time he brings a friend with him. They beg for a slice of bread, or just a glass of water. The next day more come. All because you gave one glass of water. Now they return the next day and the next. What are you going to do? Peggy, there are too many of them, you cannot help them all.

"Now you are asking how much they get paid. Well, I will tell you a little story about what happened to me. It was when Simba was just a small toddler. I knew that if I used my secretarial skills I could make more money for our struggling family, and I pay almost nothing for a babysitter. I hired an older black woman for just three rands a day. I knew this was very little, but she was thrilled to have a job and thought it was plenty.

"One day little Simba was playing on the floor right by where this woman was ironing. She went to get the phone and while she was gone, Simba pulled the iron over on himself. It burned his leg. He was asleep for the night when I got home, so I didn't see the sore until the next day. I thought about this very carefully. I knew the woman needed this job, but what upset me most was that she didn't tell me. If she was so scared of losing her job, maybe other things would happen that she would not tell me about also.

"I decided I had to let her go. I decided to stay home with my children instead of work. When I had to tell the woman, it broke my heart. She started to cry and plead with me. I was so torn."

Before my trip I had read an article in a National Geographic magazine that confirmed what she was saying. It said something to the effect that if a black man and a white man in Namibia are working at the exact same job, the white man always gets paid more. I didn't know if this was true for South Africa too, but now I see that it is. With no minimum wage and the blacks or coloreds not being paid what they are worth, then this country has created a monster. Desperate people! It's like Tansy said, "Peggy, if people will work for nothing, then why would anyone pay them more?"

So what have some of these desperate people resorted to? Stealing. At least it puts food on their table. I am not trying to justify stealing; stealing is wrong. But I can't say what I'd do. It just seems that this whole thing wouldn't be if from the beginning they were treated equal. It seemed so simple to

Tansy and me, but we were just two little women floating in a sea of injustice.

On the weekend we had a blast. Tansy and I would make up some things for a picnic. Then we would all get into the car and go on an adventure. We would drive and drive. On Saturday we all went to the beach. Nkosi liked his newspaper so he would sit and read while Tansy, Tembeka, Simba, and I hung out together. Everywhere we went, people would stare. In South Africa you never see whites and blacks being friends and having fun together. I would get stares of disgust from white people and stares from black men as if I were available. There were definitely different kinds of stares. At first it bothered me, but I soon got used to it and just paid no attention to it.

We really stood out at the beach, me with my winter-white skin and Tansy with her native black skin. We were all sitting under Tansy's umbrella, burying Simba in the sand. We couldn't help but notice that some of the white people had been laying out so long, they were beginning to turn colored. This gave rise to a discussion of skin. I suggested that, maybe the black people were the lucky ones. Their skin was so dark that you couldn't see any flaws. White people on the other hand have skin problems, which seem to be more noticeable. Moles, freckles, blackheads, even the hair on our legs shows up if we don't shave regularly. I couldn't even see any hair on Tembeka's or Tansy's legs. I said, "See this brown freckle on my arm? Now if I could get all of my skin this color you wouldn't be able to see it, would you?"

This conversation reminded Tembeka of a question she had had, "What's a blackhead? I have always wondered. I heard them say 'blackhead' on the TV, and I didn't know what that was."

I tried to explain it to her, but she had never seen one before.

"That's just exactly what I'm talking about," I replied. "Tembeka, you're a lucky girl."

Tansy by now was laughing her head off about this whole conversation and Tembeka was being nothing but serious.

After the beach we went over to beautiful Hoot Bay and bought fish and chips. Nkosi saw a man who taught at his school; he was with his family. He came over and Nkosi introduced us, and the man and his family joined us. Nkosi seemed to enjoy introducing me as their friend from America so I was always a curiosity. People stared when we all sat down to eat our fish together. People were simply amazed at a lone white woman sitting at lunch with two black families, but I didn't mind at all. I always enjoyed being with the Manjanis.

We drove to where the Atlantic Ocean meets the Indian Ocean. It was quite amazing. The Atlantic Ocean is so cold that it hurts to put your foot in. The Indian Ocean is warmer like southern California in the summer. Where the two meet you can put your feet in on one side and feel the cold. Then within walking distance you can put your feet in and it's warm. The beaches on the warm side are filled with people swimming, but the beaches on the cold side are practically deserted. It was all in all a beautiful day and I was having the time of my life.

Sunday rolled around and Tansy said, "Do you want to go to my church or yours?"

Tansy had taken the time to find one of my churches in Cape Town, but I replied, "Yours, of course. I can go to my church anytime, but I crossed the ocean just to go with you."

She was excited. Then Nkosi announced he was going.

"Why? You never want to go." Tansy said.

"Well, I figured it being the New Year and all."

"Just say it. You want to impress Peggy."

"Okay, so what's wrong with that?"

I was impressed too. I had seen religion bring people closer together, but I had also seen it force people further apart. Nothing else brings so much love, yet nothing else has brought so much hate. Whether it has come out in wars and awful bloodshed, or whether it lies locked up inside someone's heart, the hate has destroyed people. I've never been able to understand that.

Although religion can't make anyone perfect, isn't it supposed to make people try? And trying is the whole reason people go, right? Well I guess that's an individual thing. Religion can't make the person. Its what's in the heart. And sometimes what's in the heart spills out, making us who we are on the outside.

We all drove into town to the Salvation Army church. It turned out to be a sermon meant just for us. I asked Nkosi why people were wearing uniforms. Were they really in the army? He tried to answer as best he knew, "People who belong to the Salvation Army are literally an army fighting against evil. They think of themselves as if they are literally God's army."

A major in this army, but also the pastor speaking to the congregation, got up and started his talk with a story. He told how he was stationed up in a remote part of Africa. He and his friend were the only whites in a whole village of black natives. The natives had strange customs and spoke no English. In fact, they were so different, that they decided to pitch a tent outside of the village, not wanting to be too close to the natives. They couldn't understand what, if any, good they would accomplish. How could they even begin to teach such heathens? The barriers were beginning to be put up. In time, they resented being there.

One night they were invited to attend one of the ceremonies in the village. Thinking it would be a good way to get involved with the natives, they consented. That night, his friend came down with a terrible headache and as luck would have it he said, "You'll have to go alone."

As it grew dark outside, he found himself sitting on the ground in the middle of a large grass hut with only a small fire burning in the center. It wasn't long before the whole room became crammed full of black people. The longer he sat there, the more uncomfortable he got. He couldn't understand a word they were saying. Soon, being uncomfortable began to turn into being afraid. He felt very alone. Now his imagination fueled his fear. He wondered if these people could be trusted. It was one of the most uncomfortable times of his life.

As the fire died down, his uneasiness grew. The night became dark, the glowing embers cast just enough light that as he looked around the room, all he could see were glowing eyes and shining teeth. Just when he thought he could take it no more, everyone in the room started to sing. Then crystal-clear music began to fill the room; it was the most beautiful music he had ever heard. Truly no angels' choir ever sounded more sweet. As he sat there listening to the music, it gently filled the shack, then like the smoke from the fire it filtered out into the night. Through the small hole in the roof, he could see the stars. They seemed somehow closer than they ever had before. It was as if heaven itself were telling him he was among angels. He began to feel a calm, peaceful feeling starting somewhere deep inside and growing until it filled his whole soul. Warmth comforted his raging heart. Down came the barriers, down came the doubts, how could all of his past emotions have turned totally upside down within a matter of a few moments? The spirit of love had replaced his fears. And when the spirit of love is this strong, it pierces your soul, making a cut so deep you never forget it.

It simply crushed all the barriers he had put up. It dissipated the fear of the unknown and replaced it with a new understanding. With the barriers down, God was able to do His work through him. He grew to love and trust those black people, and they grew to love Him.

This story led into his sermon on tearing down barriers thus allowing God to do His work through us. Barriers, we all have them; we put them up to protect ourselves, creating them out of fear, misunderstandings, and anger. It is easier to just stay where we feel most comfortable.

Miracles can only happen through us. When someone prays for help, what can God do if we have put up barriers? How can He send a message to us that He needs our help? We are His only instruments. His work gets done through us.

Everyone will need help sometime in their lives. If it doesn't come from others, where will it come from? We live in a world starving for love. People are in need of love, not material things. The best things in life aren't things, they're people. But we've put up barriers. We decide who we will like and who we will not. And none of us are willing to cross that line. Look at South Africa, people living in fear, people full of hate. Nobody needs to let down their barriers more. If we do not, it will only continue to get worse.

As I looked around the room, I began to see people, the same people who are in every church. There's the man sitting alone on the back row. To look at him you can see he's had a hard life, but he came here to find some peace through Jesus.

There's the family on the front row with a mom and a dad, both working together to keep the kids quiet.

There's the three sisters coming in alone, because their husbands have the idea they don't need religion.

Then there's the choir. They aren't exactly sounding like angels but they give it all they've got because they are touched and they hope others will be too.

Maybe it's time we looked at all the things we have in common instead of all our differences. A feeling of love came over me for all these people sitting here trying as hard as they knew how to do what God wants them to do. A feeling I can't begin to describe came over me as I looked down the row and even Nkosi was touched, turning to wipe a tear from his eye. It was beautiful and we all felt it.

I didn't know the songs but I felt like singing out loud. I knew Simba and Tembeka were staring at me because this was a side of their Auntee they hadn't seen before. Today I felt like the luckiest person in the world, these wonderful people sitting next to me loved me and I loved them and there isn't a thing in the world more beautiful and satisfying than that.

Since I've known Tansy I've thought of myself as the giver and she the receiver. Only because I had more money. This was a selfish way to think. It turns out that she has given me so much more than I could have ever given her. I felt so close to her at that moment, it was as if she were my own sister. If it wasn't for her, I wouldn't have my two heroes, Tansy and Wynoma.

When people reach out to others outside of their comfort zone, that's when the real miracles begin to happen. We felt such a love after that meeting that I can't even describe it. I guess God has a way of doing that. We came out of there arm in arm and we didn't care who was staring.

On the way home we all tried to sing songs that everyone knew. I think it was because Tembeka heard me singing out loud at her church. We probably didn't sound all that good but nobody cared how it sounded; the way we felt inside, made it sound good to us.

Please, never let me grow old so that
I lose the innocence . . . and the trust,
of my youth.

8

Auntee

Today Simba and Tembeka were going to take me on a real adventure. We planned that I would pick them up right after school, bring a change of clothes (they didn't want to wear their school uniforms), and we'd be off. I had mentioned that I would like to do some shopping for souvenirs for my family back home. Tembeka said, "I know right where to take you."

It was hard for me to decide which was safer, traveling by myself or with the kids. We drove for about an hour. The whole time I kept hearing things such as, "Turn here, I think it's here."

"Tembeka, you know it's the next street."

"Turn right."

"No, Simba not here."

"Yes, I know it's here."

We started to go by what Simba thought, because Tembeka wasn't sure anymore.

The whole while I was trying to remain calm. I was driving on a freeway at fifty kilometers an hour and I hadn't a clue where I was. Then I said, "You guys, I kind of need to know a little bit ahead of time what exit we are going to take, not right as I am about to pass it up. Okay?"

Then I thought to myself, what on earth made me believe that a nine year old could ever show me around a city that was even new to him?

After a long silence Tembeka hesitantly whispered to Simba, "Where are we, Simba? I told you it was the last one."

Simba replied, half sure, "I think you can get to it this way too."

Finally we were smack dab in the most crowded place I have ever driven in. The streets were so narrow it didn't look like two cars could fit down them. As if I wasn't already nervous enough, one of those taxi vans Nkosi warned me about was right on my bumper, honking at me.

There were so many people right in the street; they were all black. It looked like one of those crazy open markets you've seen on TV somewhere in India or something. Everyone had set up little booths and they were selling everything from fruit to furniture, right in the street.

Of course, the children didn't worry about such things, or even notice, but I was the one and only white person there. I hated to bring it to the kids' attention, but I did feel a bit out of place. I calmly asked, "Is it okay for white people to shop here?"

What I really meant was, is it safe here?

"Oh, sure, anyone can shop here."

"Okay then, let's find a place to park."

No problem. I found one of those "help-you-park-it men," and this time I was very glad to see him. He guided me to a parking spot then announced, "I watch your car, madam!"

We shopped and got stared at for about an hour. The children kept asking, "What stores do you have in America? Do you have this one?"

"No."

"Do you have this one?"

"No."

Finally I saw a Levi's store and exclaimed, "We have this one?" The children and "Auntee Peggy" were having such an exciting time together.

Up ahead I saw a welcome sight that almost brought a tear to my eye. A McDonalds, just like back home. I couldn't believe it. The food tasted just like back home, and I bought a Big Mac for about twenty cents. I told the kids they could have anything they wanted, but they were very conservative with their orders. It seemed so strange to be ordering all American food from people who spoke very broken English. We returned to the car with its faithful watchman at his post. I thanked him and paid him and we were off again.

We went to look at the old apartment building where they said they lived before I came. Then they took me to Tembeka's old school where I met her principal, and on to Simba's school where I fell in love with the gardens. There were so many different kinds of flowers that I recognized from back home.

Tansy had explained to me how they had to find for the children a school that was primarily English-speaking. Her children had had a problem learning so many different languages. By the time they were five they were speaking in sentences mixing words from three different languages. Now here in South Africa they wanted them to learn a fourth, Afrikaans. So they made a concrete decision that they would speak only English to their children. Finding an all English-speaking school was next to impossible, so the school they are in now teaches primarily English with a little Afrikaans thrown in.

All the children wear uniforms and they are very strict when it comes to jewelry and braids; neither are accepted. They want all the children to be the same. In some ways that's good, because they have kids coming from different economic levels, and hopefully they can all be treated equal.

As we drove around, I couldn't help noticing the huge, beautiful homes each surrounded by either a fence made of brick with barbed wire at the top or stone with broken bottle pieces on top. There wasn't a single house that didn't have cast-iron bars on all the windows and doors. The bars were molded into beautiful designs; the more the wealth, the more intricate the design. It almost disguised the very purpose of the bars, which was to keep the thieves out. The white people had so much more than the blacks, but instead of helping with the poverty they were simply saying, "Try to steal from me, I'll just make it so you can't."

If you wonder why the black people are stealing---and I am not saying it is right---you will be able to understand it better if you read *Kaffir Boy* by Mark Mathabane.

We got back pretty late and Tansy was worried about us. With me driving two little black kids around, we do stick out. Tembeka promptly told her mom about Auntee telling the man at the gas station to fill it up. He just stood there staring. Tansy laughed and said, "No one around here says, 'Fill it up;' no one can afford to fill it up."

That must be why I had to tell him three times and then try to explain it to him. He went and got his buddy; they just sat there staring at us. It was the first time I heard Tembeka say, "I'm tired of people staring at us."

Simba just couldn't wait to tell his mom, "Auntee hit the car into the curb and hit another car's mirror."

I felt that I needed to clear myself so I told her I hated her streets; they were too narrow. I said a taxi was behind me pressing down hard. It made me so nervous, I hit into the curb. She just laughed and said, "That happens to me all the time."

She said she had become used to just holding her own. "Don't let them make you nervous; just get out of their way when you feel like it."

Tansy had planned to take us all to the botanical gardens the next day. Nkosi was out of town on a staff meeting. She made snacks to take with us. She had even bought sliced lunchmeat, a luxury to them. In the next few weeks she bought a lot of luxuries; I knew it was just for me. I was honored, but at the same time I felt bad, because she would never let me help pay for them, and I knew it was setting them back.

The botanical gardens were absolutely the most beautiful I had ever seen, and I had seen many different ones in the States. In Cape Town there was a mountain known as Table Mountain. It is completely flat on top. One side is dry and the other side always has a cloud hanging over it, which Simba called the tablecloth. On the shady, wet side of Table Mountain sits Kirstenbosch Botanical Gardens. We discovered a trail that led out of the gardens all the way up to the top of the Table. Tansy was out of shape, but stubborn. She insisted on carrying all the drinks, all the fruit, and all the snacks. We soon tired and turned back to save that hike for another day.

The gardens had huge mysterious trees. I am, by nature and by profession, a flower nut, but the trees here held my greatest attention. I had never seen trees like this. There were trees with enormous trunks at the bottom and ferns on top. There were weird trees called cycads, that looked like something out of the dinosaur age, and tall old trees with paths leading right through their roots. It was all out of this world. It was Disneyland for plant lovers! I wanted to buy some flower seeds to take home, but they were closed, so we would have to come back another day. "Oh for shame!" Tansy teased, as she knew I would love to return.

That night a black musical band came on TV. Tansy knew a few of the songs. Since Nkosi wasn't home and the kids were in bed, she started dancing, singing, and acting totally stupid. She doesn't get to let her fun side out very often, because Nkosi is always being so calm and reserved. "It's no fun to be this way around him," she complained.

We both got a little crazy as if we were two teenage girls with the sillies.

The next night we walked down to the phone booth so Tansy could call her sisters back in Zambia. She didn't like to use her home phone because she was afraid it would be too easy to talk too long, and it is very expensive. So she would save up a few extra rands, and when her money ran out so did her phone call. After she hung up and we were walking back I asked Tansy if she was doing okay. I hadn't seen her sad over her mother passing away. I was concerned that she needed time to mourn. I told Tansy it's okay if you need to cry in front of me; I truly don't mind.

She just smiled and said, "I would have been so sad but just knowing you were coming made me feel so happy. I have been having such a good time with you. I told my sisters, my friend from the States is here, so I'm okay. There will be plenty of time to mourn when you're gone, then I'll be doing double mourning."

We needed a real woman-to-woman talk so we just told Nkosi to watch the kids and took a drive that night. We didn't know where we were going but it didn't matter. We wanted to talk with no interruptions. We talked about marriages and how they can become when you're our age. You've been together for so long you wonder if you're both becoming bored and boring.

I knew that Tansy had always fought with these struggles. Nkosi is so different from her. She is funny and loud around her friends and Nkosi doesn't like that about her. To him she is too loud and very bossy, to her he is too quiet and boring. But together they have moved around so much that they have needed each other. Lots of times each other was all they had, and now she feels they are more like best friends than husband and wife. They really do need each other. Sometimes it helps just having someone say, "So what's wrong with that? Many husbands and wives aren't even best friends. And look at all we like about him. He's a good father to the children, he is stable like a rock, he is kind, he is loving. He loves you, Tansy, and I know it."

We had a good talk, and although we will never be able to solve each other's problems, it sure felt good to try. We shared our closest feelings deep into the night. I felt so thankful for the gift of a true and trusted friend.

After work Tansy wanted me to meet two of her best friends, both from Zambia. One, a mother to one of Simba's best friends, and the other whose husband went to school with Nkosi back in Zambia. One was absolutely the most beautiful black woman I had ever seen. Her husband had gone back to Zambia to find work but she hadn't heard from him in several months. She was very worried. The other lived in one of the better townships available. They felt they would never have enough money for a real house. Both were equally kind and friendly when I visited with them. Tansy must have wanted them to really get to know me, because as soon as she introduced me she never said another word until it was time to leave. We talked and shared so easily; I could have become best of friends with either of these two girls, yet I know that under any other circumstances we probably would have never met.

On the way home Tansy told me a story about when she was in the hospital. She got to know the lady in the bed next to hers who was from one of the poorest townships. Tansy knew it well because she had once lived there. They were becoming good friends, so she told the lady she would come visit her when they got out. If a black person does get ahead they are sometimes quick to forget the others from where they started. Tansy kept her word and went to visit her.

When the lady saw her coming she couldn't believe her eyes. She said, "You didn't have to come, in fact, I knew you wouldn't."

Tansy explained to her that she considered her just the same as any of her other good friends. It's not where you live that makes you who you are, it's what's on the inside---and she liked her inside. To this day she and Tansy are still friends.

Tansy said she had made a promise to herself that if she ever did get ahead in this life, she would never forget others and think she was now better than them.

The next weekend we were all off to the tippiest end of the African continent, the Cape of Good Hope. They have a park there and you can see all kinds of animals, baboons, ostriches, strange-colored antelope and so on; and we did see all kinds of animals. Twice Tansy scared Nkosi nearly to death because we had our window down and all these baboons were around. They started to come right up to our car, which made Nkosi very nervous. He was watching a mother and her baby right out of my window, but his arm was leaning out of his. Tansy grabbed it from behind and made some loud baboon noise. He jumped up, hit his head on the ceiling, and yelled. We all had to hold our sides we were laughing so hard.

We had made a picnic for the beach; it was our own version of Kentucky Fried Chicken and potato salad. As we sat down to eat we noticed the sand looked like tiny glass rocks, each particle polished bright and shining in the sun. I had never tried to take a picture from my new camera using the timer; we sure had fun trying though. Each time I turned the timer on, everyone would yell, "Hurry, come sit by me!" Then, click! it would go off before we were ready. What a fun day!

That night we were sitting around the kitchen table talking. We noticed some bright lights right outside our door; they were police lights. Nkosi said, "It looks like it is coming from next door."

He went over to check it out. When he came back he informed us that someone had been stabbed right outside on our sidewalk. The man dragged himself to the neighbor's house who then called the police. I didn't know what to think; this kind of life was so different to me. At home we never even lock our doors and we go out at night for walks all the time. They could have just as easily ended up at the Manjanis door.

I went to bed restless that night; I had two things on my mind. The first was the things I had seen while I had been in South Africa. I remembered an incident that I couldn't stop thinking about. I was at an intersection one day. A black man had thought of a job for himself. When the light was red he would hurry and wash your windows. The kind thing to do was to pay him a few cents. I saw a very expensive car pull up. I don't know too many kinds of cars but it was like a Mercedes-Benz or a BMW. The lady sat in her car with all the windows up, air-conditioning on full blast, wearing some real fancy sunglasses. He hurried and washed her window so it sparkled. She sat there, allowing him to take care of her, then just as soon as the light changed, she sped off.

Would she have missed one rand? Not in the slightest, yet she just didn't want to bother.

As I sat there I remembered a contrasting story that Tansy told me about her mother in Zambia. The hospitals in Zambia were getting so overcrowded, no one could think of a way to convince the poor Zambian women to stop bringing children into the world if they couldn't supply them with their basic needs. So they came up with a plan. Women could not take their babies home from the hospital if they could not supply at least three nappies (diapers) and one T-shirt for that child. It sounds harsh, but they had tried telling them and telling them, but nothing had worked. A woman came to Tansy's mom and begged her for three nappies and a T-shirt. Being poor, but wanting to help, she made her the diapers and the shirt. The next year that same woman came again begging for three nappies and a T-shirt. Tansy's mom gave her those things again. The third time when she came, Tansy's mom gave her the items but this time she warned her, "If you come again, I will not give to you any more."

When she came the fourth time it broke her mom's heart to turn her away, but she felt she had no choice. This was the exact reason the hospital had made this rule. She turned her away and shut the door, leaned against it, and cried.

Wynoma, Tansy's mother, believed, "Maybe you can't give to all, but you can give to some. Giving something is better than not giving at all."

The homes with fences and bars, the men parking cars and washing windows, the stabbing---all of it bothered me.

The second thing on my mind was the fact that I had been in Africa almost a month and I hadn't seen any other part of the continent. The last few nights I had thought about going to Victoria Falls. I felt that I had come this far and to be so close and never see it I would regret it the rest of my life. Nkosi had told me it was in his native land Zambia, another reason to go.

I knew that under the circumstances the Manjanis couldn't take me, but that didn't keep me from wanting to go.

So, after some tremendous thought, I had come up with an idea: I would take a bus there.

The next morning I called Greyhound, but they don't have buses going there. Then I called Translux; they no longer had buses going there ever since the threat to tourists in Johannesburg. Last of all I called the city bus called the Intercape. Yes, they had a bus that goes there, only instead of heading back up the coast of South Africa, it went up through Namibia. It would take three days and two nights with a twelve-hour layover in Vintage. I couldn't even pronounce Namibia, let alone know where Vintage is, but who cared as long as I ended up at Victoria Falls. I was all excited but a little nervous to tell Tansy. So I told Nkosi first.

He thought it was a great idea. But what would I tell my husband Scott? Just as I feared. When I talked to my Scott on the phone he said, "Absolutely not. I don't want you riding alone on some strange bus in the middle of Africa!"

Gee, he made it sound *so* unreasonable.

Well I couldn't get it out of my mind. I asked Nkosi again and he said he thought it would be perfectly safe. I figured I am here and I see that things aren't so bad. Now I must convince Scott of that. So I tried a different approach. This time when I talked to Scott I told him he had the wrong idea. I would be taking a tour bus full of tourists, and I would meet someone on the bus to hang out with. It's all just a guided tour. I didn't want him to worry and I felt perfectly confident.

"Well, okay, but be careful."

"Yes!"

I asked Nkosi if he would take me to get some tickets. My original plan was to see the Falls then turn right around and come back home---no big deal. But on checking into it more, the bus only left the Falls on Sundays. That meant I would get there on Tuesday afternoon and have to stay until Sunday.

By now Tansy had heard about it and she insisted she would not let me go unless I went to talk to her friend who was working for the embassy of Zimbabwe.

It turned out to be a good visit with her friend. She told me she would call the embassy in Johannesburg. They could find lodging for me in Zimbabwe; then once I'm up there I could take a taxi anywhere I wanted for just a dollar a day. They even had some guided tours I could take. Most of them cost way too much money for this budget trip. Then it was set.

Nkosi, the children, and I were off to get bus tickets when we hit a traffic jam. Nkosi said, "This is strange; there is never a traffic jam this time of day."

As we got closer he said, "Oh, I know what this is. I bet someone got hit by a car."

He told me they couldn't get the colored people to stop trying to outrun the cars on the freeway so they built a pedestrian overwalk just a few meters up ahead. Yet they still try to outrun the cars.

Sure enough, there on the pavement lay a little boy. It was so sad. I looked over just in time to see two little feet wearing two different kinds of shoes. He was dead. I will never forget those little feet. I hoped the children didn't see.

At the bus station it was more of the same. Some black men wanted to help us park our car. Nkosi could never say no to these people. There were people all over either trying to sell you things or begging. I don't know if I could ever get used to it. I noticed it all. The sounds of people calling to you to buy their wares, even when I was standing in an empty bus station trying to buy my ticket. Outside you could hear all this yelling. Nkosi finally asked, "What is that?"

The man behind the desk remarked, "Oh, it's those men trying to sell their fruit." He sounded real perturbed.

Nkosi said, "Does all that yelling help?"

"Oh, I don't know?" now getting very irritated. He took my visa card. This was the first time I had used it on my whole trip. I was curious to see if it worked. It did, and I thought, small world. He handed me a round-trip ticket and the first thing I noticed were the words, "Half the adventure is getting there."

When we got home, Tansy was putting on an act. I knew she didn't want me to go because that would mean less time I would have to spend with her. But she tried to act excited for me anyway. She was a true friend. That night was another hard one for me to get any sleep. Tansy told me this would be such an experience. I would be leaving a first world country and traveling into a third world country. I couldn't get those words out of my mind, the ones on the bus ticket, "Half the adventure is getting there." I hoped so.

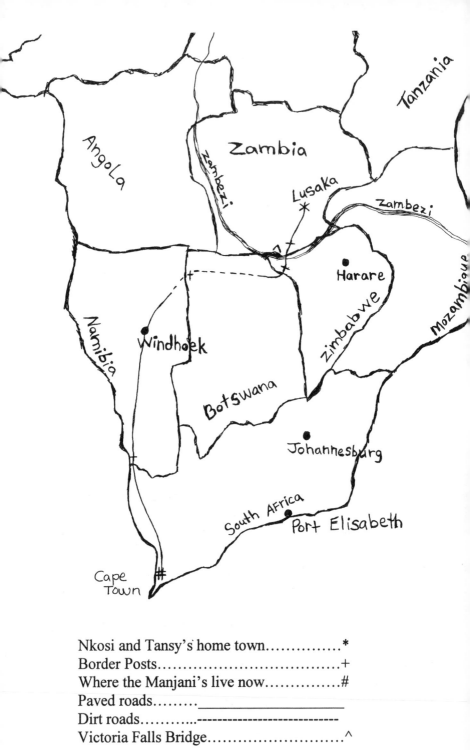

Nkosi and Tansy's home town...............*
Border Posts...................................+
Where the Manjani's live now...............#
Paved roads........._____
Dirt roads...........-----------------------------
Victoria Falls Bridge..........................^

*It is difficult, if not impossible, to return
an act of kindness, a genuine smile,
with anger or resentment.*

9

The Bus

I am filled with excitement today. Have you ever noticed on those days when everything is going your way, and you're about to embark on an adventure, people don't bug you like they usually do? Life is great.

Well, today is one of those days for me. With all the technicalities out of the way, I am on my way to the Salvation Army to attend their church meeting, eager to hear all the good words, let them fill my soul, then take them with me on the bus.

Tansy and Tembeka are with me. I'm feeling especially fond of them right now. We dropped Tembeka off for Sunday School and now the two of us have an hour to kill. Tansy surprised me by taking me to a Sunday craft fair in town. There were people from all over Africa there to sell their wares.

She kept telling me not to buy too much here, because things will be much cheaper up in Zambia. I couldn't resist these tiny hand-carved elephants. It was the whole herd from the biggest to the littlest, marching in a line. Thirty-five rands. Okay, I'll take them.

Just then I got this funny feeling. *Ah, oh.* Tansy is going to pour out some of her wisdom on me. She gets this kind of motherly instinct prodding her then feels that it is her duty to educate me. I feel sometimes she thinks of me as a little kid who just stepped out of the back yard for the first time. Now she must warn me of all the hidden dangers in this big bad world.

This time she warned me not to take the first offer but to bargain about it for a while. But to me it was worth thirty-five rands, so what was there to bargain about? I bought it. Tansy just smiled.

Then I sat my purse down to talk with a man about his wares. When I was finished, Tansy pulled me aside and said. "I must tell you about your purse. You never set it down while you talk; you hold it to you. See this strap? It is to wear; keep it on you at all times. Peggy, you are too trusting."

I guess I've always looked at that different than most folks. It was said best to me by my father when I was just a teenager, "Peggy, never trust anyone until they prove they can be trusted."

That seemed to be a scared man's way to live. So I said, "No, Dad, I think I am going to trust everyone until they prove they *can't* be trusted."

Ooh, to him *that* was a scary way to live.

So I don't think of myself as actually careless. Trusting, yes, careless, never. Hadn't I brought twelve hundred rands with me? (Nkosi said to take rands because they would be easier to use than American money.) I had put four hundred in my purse, four hundred in my backpack, and four hundred in my nylon bag, all of which I would carry with me onto the bus. I figured if someone stole my purse that would be okay, I almost expected that to happen. So then I would go to my backup, and I had two backups! I decided not to take any luggage with me that I could not see at all times.

I was not heading into this adventure totally blind; I knew I would meet desperate people. I knew how poor Zambia was. That's why I was carrying extra shoes and skirts so I could give some away.

When we got to church, Tembeka had saved us a place. We sat down, said our hellos to some of Tansy's friends, and listened and sang and just enjoyed being there.

After it was over, Tansy took me to the bus station. We bought some fruit from one of those noisy vendors. I put it in my now bulging backpack and went to board the bus. I asked the lady who was taking tickets if I could carry both bags on with me. I was small so I could put one under the seat by my feet and the other one in front of it. Somehow I forgot about legroom.

If I was going to be on this bus for three days and two nights I was going to be prepared. Tissues, anti-bacterial lotions and soaps, two bottles of mosquito repellent---"Deep Woods Off," no less---for malaria protection, six big bottled waters, paper for my journal, and, of course, food enough to last me for days. This was going to be a very low-budget trip.

I was down to the last of my money. I planned on eating out once and eating out of my bag the rest of the time. Ever get sick of bananas? Well, maybe I hadn't thought of everything. I just didn't want to spend my money on dumb food; I wanted to buy trinkets to take home to my family and friends.

Just then the bus pulled up. It was one of those two-story buses. I ran up to be the first in line. The lady taking tickets told me to sit upstairs. I went right up and suddenly forgot I hadn't said goodbye to Tansy and Tembeka. I looked out the window and they were waving at me frantically. I pushed my way back through the crowd to get off.

"I want you to try real hard to get by a window," Tansy encouraged, "I know how you like to look out at everything everywhere you go."

"Okay, thank you. This is it."

Goodbyes were said and we gave big hugs, and I was off. I knew Tansy was sad to see me go. It would mean losing ten days of the time we planned on spending together. It was hard for both of us yet part of her was glad that now all the places she had told me about would come to life for me. She knew I was excited to see the jungles, the farms, and just to get out of the city.

That's how it goes when you really care for someone. You forget your own selfishness and you are happy simply because you know they are happy.

By now I was used to people staring. This whole trip I had yet to see a white woman and a black woman enjoying each other's company. It was no different when I got on the bus; people were staring at me as usual.

Now that I was on the bus I began my quest. I needed to find someone else going to see the Falls so I wouldn't have to travel alone. The more I looked around, the more I could see this was not a tour bus: people carrying shopping bags, people speaking all different languages, all different accents, and no other American on the bus. Oh well, I hadn't seen another American my whole trip, why should this be any different?

There were mostly black people and a few white people from Europe who called themselves "backpackers." This was my first experience with backpackers. However, the lady at the embassy told me about backpackers inns. She said, "You can stay there for three American dollars per night but I can't guarantee what you'll find. Maybe running water, maybe not, maybe accessible to food, maybe not, and no guarantee you'll be safe. They are a breed of their own."

They were mostly college-age kids who come down from Europe. They want to see the world but have very little money. They carry their sleeping bags with them everywhere and don't mind the primitive accommodations. I didn't know if I could fit in with them but I wouldn't mind their company.

The first thing I saw after leaving Cape Town were the farms. For the first time on my trip I felt at home. I love to see growing things. At home we own a small farm. We have raspberries, strawberries, blackberries and we also planted every kind of fruit tree we could think of.

Now there were rolling hills covered in grapevines and what I thought looked like banana trees. Oh, it was soothing to my soul. I recognized most crops, there were only a few I didn't know. Maybe sugar cane? Maybe some kind of fruit trees? Maybe, I don't know, I was just having fun guessing.

As we got farther north in South Africa it became more primitive. Now the bus began stopping at a few game reserves where people got off to join their tour guides. Their guides would be waiting for them in some old dust-covered jeeps, just like in the movies. As I watched this spectacle, a young woman sat down by me and asked to see my passport.

On the bus you have a bus attendant who comes around to give you the proper papers you will need to get into the other countries. They check your passports and occasionally bring around coffee and tea to drink. This attendant was a young black woman with a strong Namibian accent. When she came around to check our passports she was surprised by my accent and knew immediately that I was an American. She smiled an extra-friendly smile and said, "Your passport, please." As I handed her my passport she looked it over carefully then, handing it back to me, she made the comment, "This is the nicest passport I have ever seen."

It always makes you feel good when someone smiles at you just to be friendly. Then she asked the question I must have been asked a hundred times on my trip, "Where in America do you live?"

It seemed that everyone had heard of California, but not a single person had heard of Utah. So I would always reply, "You've heard of California, right?"

"Yes."

"Well, Utah is real close to there."

She was the first of many friendly blacks I would meet on this trip. She handed me a package of oatmeal cookies and said, "Enjoy your stay in Namibia."

I began to lie back in my chair and watch comfortably out the window. Then the sound of a movie came over the speakers. The television screen in front of us didn't work, but as soon as I heard the first sentence, I recognized it. It was *Titanic*. Listening to something so familiar, so American, made me feel peaceful inside.

I began writing in my journal. It is good to be alone now and then. That's the time when you really find out who you are. You have no one to rely on but yourself. That's when you do some real soul-searching and just take time to think. Boy, did I have a lot of time to think on this trip!

The bus slowed down, jerked a bit, and stopped. We all waited. We were all strangers, yet I didn't feel alone. Someone said, "Oh great, the bus broke down."

I heard a few more under-the-breath comments. Everyone seemed perturbed, yet no one showed any anger.

I didn't mind as long as it didn't take more than ten hours to fix. I knew I had to kill twelve hours waiting for the next bus in Windhoek, Namibia, anyway.

When I called to get bus tickets I thought they said, "With a twelve hour layover in Vintage."

Nkosi said, "I have never heard of Vintage, Namibia. Could it be Windhoek, Namibia?"

I didn't know until I purchased my tickets that it was Windhoek, the capital of Namibia. Nkosi had a good friend teaching at the University of Windhoek. If I ran into any trouble I could get in touch with him. It's good to have many friends; you never know when you'll need someone.

I was on a tight schedule. When I got back to Cape Town I would have only three days until my plane was scheduled to leave and take me back to the States.

We sat there for about two hours. Then the attendant's voice came over the speaker, "I'm sorry for the inconvenience, but we will have to return to the last town we just passed through," she said in her beautiful Namibian accent.

Just then some guy on the bus stood up and went outside. I could see him talking with the bus driver. They worked together for some time. They got the bus going again, and we were off.

When the lights inside the bus came on they made it impossible to see anything outside, so we all tried to sleep.

About eleven o'clock, or as they say in Africa, 2300 hours, we reached the Namibia border post. It was my first border-post experience. I was a little nervous about this one because I did not have a visa to get into Namibia. I had called when I was in the States to see if I needed a separate visa (besides my passport) to get into Botswana, Zimbabwe, and Zambia. But I did not check on Namibia at that time because I didn't know I would be going there.

Everyone had to get off the bus and go into this tiny dirty building and show their passport. We formed a single-file line. You never knew what to expect from these border officials. You were now at their mercy since you were trying to get into their country, and they knew it.

Things were going pretty smoothly until they came to me. They took a l-o-n-g look at my passport, then at the customs paper I had filled out, then back at me. There was a long pause then, as he began to speak, I could hardly understand him.

"Where are you staying in Namibia?"

"I am not staying in Namibia. I will arrive at Windhoek in the morning, then I will wait twelve hours to catch another bus and go on to Victoria Falls."

Another long pause.

"You show me on this map which way you are traveling."

I stood there staring at the map and realized for the first time that I had no idea which way I was going. I never thought about asking what roads we were going to take to get there, I just knew the bus would get me there. I looked up at his map. I couldn't even find Victoria Falls on the map.

Just then the bus driver came up to the desk. He said to the official, "This woman is riding the bus to Victoria Falls. She . . ."

The official cut him off. "What are you answering for? I am asking her! She can talk for herself!"

He was getting very rude.

I interrupted, "Um, the problem is, I can't find Victoria Falls on your map."

He looked up at his old dirty map, stared at it for a while, and then stared at me. He then grunted something under his breath while he stamped my passport and said, "Next!"

So started the beginning of many a border-post experience.

That night was beautiful. All the lights in the bus were off now. A full moon hung over the desert. The air was so clear; that moon seemed massive. With the silhouettes of the big African trees against that moon and in that clear air everything was illuminated and seemed almost unreal.

It's hard to get back to sleep on a bus once you wake up. Now I was wide-awake. I sat there in the stillness, staring out the window, listening to the hum of the bus, trying to let everything sink into my memory so I could take it all home with me. I expected to see a long lanky giraffe any minute, because the landscape looked like the Kalahari Desert I'd seen on the National Geographic specials, and they were always filled with animals.

On the bus there was a black man who was a little too friendly for my liking. He found a young girl to pick up on so he was being exceptionally friendly to her. They were sitting right behind me so I could clearly hear all that was being said. She didn't seem too bothered by him.

I heard her say she was from Holland, traveling to see her sister. She said her boyfriend was going to meet her at her sister's house. What followed made me feel real fortunate to be hearing such sweet human nature flowing out between such an unlikely pair.

The black man said, "Tell me a story about your home, Holland."

Then she began to tell him, in the cutest way, the legendary story of the boy who put his finger in the dike and saved all of Holland from complete destruction. My mother had told me that story when I was a child, so I knew it well. Listening to her, I noted she didn't miss a thing.

Then she said, "Now I have told you a story about where I am from, you tell me a story from where you are from."

He began to tell some kind of folk tale about the curse put on a tree because of the hyenas.

"There is a tree you can see during the dry seasons in Africa. When all the leaves fall off it, the top of it looks just like the tree is upside down. That is because the hyenas would not stop stealing all of the other animals' food. And because at the end of the day the hyenas loved to lie in the shade of this tree, the tree turned itself upside down. And it is still that way today. It is called the upside down tree."

She laughed quietly.

I couldn't help but think what different worlds these two came from; but for a few hours on a quiet bus they didn't seem that distant.

At 6:00 A.M. I arrived in Windhoek, Namibia, a city that had been settled by Germans. It was dark and deserted now. Everyone must still be asleep. The bus dropped us off at a little box of a building they called a bus station. Twelve hours now began to seem like a long, long time.

Friend,
I study the qualities I see in you
they will in turn . . . hopefully,
make up the greater part,
of who I am.

10
Windhoek

The bus station in Windhoek Namibia consisted of two desks, four telephones, one drink machine, and two small bathrooms. The first thing I did was call Tansy because she wanted me to be sure to call as soon as I had my first stop.

Nkosi answered. Tansy had already left for work. I told him I had arrived in Windhoek and I had a fairly pleasant trip. He said, "Is there a bus station there? Last time I was there, there wasn't."

"Yes, but it is very small."

"Oh, I'm glad. . . . Thank you for calling. . . . Are you going to call my friend? . . . Peggy, please call when you get to Vic Falls, okay?"

"Well, maybe. Thanks again, goodbye."

As soon as I hung up the phone I walked outside to sit on the bench. No sooner had I done so than I heard a man say, "Sorry?"

I didn't hear him clearly. He cleared his throat. "S-o--r--r-y?"

People around here were always saying sorry. With their accent it sounded like so-ree. Sorry, for excuse me, sorry, for pardon me, sorry, even when someone falls down. I couldn't help noticing it. So one day I said, "Tansy, why should you say you're sorry when someone falls down and you didn't push them?"

She had never thought of it that way before.

"It's just what we say without thinking about it."

I started to say sor-ee just to tease, trying to put as much of their accent into it as I could. Tansy and Tembeka would always get a good laugh out of it.

Now back came the voice, "Sor-ee."

"Oh, are you talking to me?"

"Yes. That will be thirty-eight dollars."

"Thirty-eight dollars! I thought that was a collect call."

"Sor-ee."

"I thought that was a collect call!" By now I was getting annoyed. I hadn't slept at all last night (I wonder why) and I felt hammered, with no mirror, and no place to wash up. He was pushing it and he didn't even know it.

"I don't have any Namibian dollars, I only have rands."

"We take rands."

There went the first of my budget-trip dollars.

I didn't dare leave my stuff unattended. So I sat down on the only bench outside the station with my two bags. I thought at the time that I would sit there all day.

As I sat there I noticed a girl sitting next to me. She was white, about twenty-five, just a bit overweight, and had a very stylish short haircut. We must have sat there for about twenty minutes with neither one daring to say anything to the other one. Finally, I thought, why not. I turned and asked, "So what bus are you waiting for?"

"The one to Vic Falls."

"Oh really, that's the one I am waiting for. What time were you told it would be here?"

"Around six tonight. Hey, do you want to leave your bags here and go for breakfast?"

She must have read my mind because she then added, "My sister said for ten rands you can ask them at the desk to watch your stuff."

"Okay."

So started my new friendship with Carol. We loved each other's accents; she struggled with her English, but I would help her out when I could. We both laughed at ourselves for being so shy; we might have sat there all day and at the end of the day we would have got on the same bus.

There was a real nice Namibian girl, about college-age, standing behind the desk; she said she would watch our bags. Carol was much more trusting than I was. She just paid her ten rands and walked off like it was no big deal.

In South Africa they had a steak house that tried to be an old western American saloon. I got a kick out of seeing colored girls dressed up as American Indians. Here in Windhoek they also had one. It was called, "The Spur." That's where Carol took me for breakfast. Carol's aunt, a South African who married a Namibian, took Carol there every time she came to stay with them. But this time she was riding the bus alone. She was going to meet them at their home about two hours from there.

As we sat there waiting for our breakfast busily talking, I blurted out, "Maybe we better go check our bags."

"I'm sure they will be okay."

That's how it went all day. I was so uneasy about leaving my bags, but she seemed to have forgotten all about hers.

After breakfast we went shopping. Carol said she loved to shop. She bought a pair of shorts, a jumper, and a few souvenirs. She shopped, I watched. It's funny, this was the first time I had gone shopping with someone overweight who seemed happy with herself and who never once mentioned her weight. I liked that about her.

Carol's aunt was her favorite person in the whole world. She said, "Every vacation I get from work I go stay with her."

Carol had lived in Cape Town her whole life. She'd had the same job ever since she got out of high school and this was as far as she had ever traveled. She loved hearing about the States. Of course, I got out my pouch of pictures, and she loved them. She had never heard of Utah. Surprise.

She talked about the violence happening in South Africa right then, but never in our whole day's conversation did she mention anything about the blacks.

We walked to a grassy hillside inside a city park filled with giant palm trees. Neither of us had slept on the bus so we felt like lying down and sleeping, but we were just too scared. It was the same as most city parks. Men were lying down under the trees either sleeping or watching people walk by. Even though we had each other we were uncomfortable in this strange city.

I just couldn't take it anymore. I had worried long enough about my camera, and my extra stashes of money, so we went back to check on our bags. I was so relieved to see that they were fine, as Carol, of course, knew they would be. We decided to walk a while.

There were these ladies who would walk by with these giant triangular hats and colorful big dresses. Carol said,

"Look, those are the Namibians' native dress." They were quite unique.

We went to a paper store. It was obvious Carol knew many of the stores because she would say, "Oh, we have one of these in Cape Town."

We looked at postcards. This was the first time I had known for sure that we had crossed the Kalahari Desert the night before. I was only guessing because it looked like the pictures I had seen. I hadn't even realized it was in Namibia. One postcard in particular caught her attention and she explained it to me, "We will be seeing these huge sand castles. They are as big as the trees, but they are actually anthills. They are all over by my aunt's house."

"Cool."

Then she wanted to go back and get a milkshake where we had had breakfast earlier that morning. She said they made the best shakes. I could go for that. It was a hot January day, I was thirsty, and I hadn't had any real milk the whole time I was in Cape Town.

"Okay, but on our way, can we go back and check on our stuff?"

Right next to the bus station there was an island in the middle of two streets. It was long and wide. There were six of the most enormous palm trees I had ever seen running down the middle. Under the trees sitting on the grass were many families selling their wares. I called them the shopping-cart families because they brought their handmade treasures there in old beat-up shopping carts. It took them all morning, making several trips back and forth from wherever they lived, often stumbling and grabbing and nearly dropping their beautiful possessions.

Each time we went back to the bus station I looked over and watched them for a while. They didn't seem to be selling much. One family had a tiny baby. Each time it began to fuss, the mom would try everything to keep it still. As the day grew hotter, and parents became more stressed about not selling their wares, tension in the little family grew. This time when we walked past, the baby was very restless and the mother was almost at her wits' end. I knew Carol was shopping for a gift for her aunt, so I stopped and bent down to get a closer look at what she was selling. Right away she picked up the baby and came to tell us that she would give us a good price. I said, "Carol, look at these beautiful hand-carved necklaces, let's buy some. I bet we can get a better price here than in the stores."

Then, as if it was the first time she had noticed them, Carol began to look at what these vendors were selling. This show of interest aroused all of the other sellers, and they begin to come alive.

"Oh, madam, come---see, I make you a deal."

"No, madam, I make you a better deal."

"Please madam, come see what I have."

I wanted to buy something from the lady with the baby, but all she had were big beautiful baskets, tall hand-carved giraffes, and elaborate drums, nothing that would fit in my little bags. I just handed her a few dollars and apologetically said, "Your baby is so beautiful, I wish I could do more. Take this and buy your baby a drink."

She thanked me. I thought, for what? I wished there was a way I could have helped everyone. Then from another family I bought some necklaces for my girls. Carol found a beautiful little hand-carved box for her aunt. Sitting in the air-conditioned room, drinking that delicious milkshake, I couldn't stop thinking about those families.

This was once again the dilemma I faced: wanting to help and feeling discouraged for not being able to do so. I could have helped some, but who?

Where do you start? These feelings stayed with me for my entire trip and are the feelings that I still carry with me to this day.

We went back to the bus station to sit and wait again. Now we had three hours left until 1800 hours when the bus should arrive. We had done all we could think of doing, so now all we could do was sit, watch, and wait.

When the bus finally did come, it was late. We were beginning to worry if it was going to come at all. You begin to form doubts in your mind the longer you wait. Are we at the right place? Do we have the right time? Is it the right day? What day is today, anyway? We asked some people standing around, and no one seemed to be waiting for our bus. I remembered the breakdown of the last bus we were on. Imagine our relief when a bus pulled in and we asked the driver, "Are you going to Vic Falls?"

He smiled and said, "Yes."

Now a few people started to appear as if out of nowhere; taxis pulled up, old broken vans pulled up. Did everyone but us know the bus would be late?

As we were boarding I showed the driver my ticket. He asked to see my passport and then he added, "Do you have money?"

Money? What a funny thing to ask. But I smiled and answered, "Yes, some."

Now as I sat by the window, waiting for all to board, I noticed the shopping-cart families all starting to pack up their belongings and head for home. It was sad that they had not sold but a few small trinkets. They had items as tall as I was, and yet with all the careful effort they had taken to bring them down, they were meticulously packing them up and carting them back. How far was home for them? I wondered as I watched them going straight up the hill and disappearing from sight. I heard someone mention the poor people sitting outside selling things.

One man interrupted, "Yes, but the real shame is that when they do sell something, most of the money goes to some guy who set up the whole deal for them."

This time there weren't many people on the bus, just a few backpackers, some black people, and Carol and I. We started talking about her home. I had hesitated all day to ask her how she felt about the coloreds and blacks in South Africa. Now I was relieved to hear her say, "I was never taught to hate anyone. I like the colored people as well as the whites. I have never taken sides. I feel it is unfortunate what has happened to the blacks but I can't help them. I am a Christian and in my church we have black people. In fact I got real close to a colored family once and when the father died of a sudden death I can still remember crying. I cried all day. Finally my mom came to me and asked me what was wrong. I told her I missed Mr. Lusaukin. She said, 'I know, we all do.'"

When she was talking about her dear friend Mr. Lusaukin, I started to realize how important Tansy was to me. None of this would be happening to me if not for her. That's when I knew it was safe to talk about my black friends.

"I know how you feel. My dear friends are black and I had hesitated to tell you because I didn't know how you felt about blacks."

"I know, I saw you hugging them before you got on the bus. I can't say why, but it was a special moment for me to reflect on how I felt about that."

As I tried to tell her how I felt about the Manjanis, she was touched and quite unexpectedly began to cry. Now we both had tears in our eyes. This was the first time I had thought about how hard it was going to be for me to say goodbye to Tansy and her little family. For some reason I had shared that sadness with Carol, someone I barely knew, but she truly felt it.

After a few quiet moments our spirits began to pick up. Carol started to teach me Afrikaans. Well, she tried. I can't remember a word of it now, but it was fun. She would touch my eyes and say something for eyes, then touch my hand and say something for hand. My hair, my nose, my forehead, I wasn't really learning anything and I'm sure people thought we were crazy. We laughed and talked until it came time for her to get off. It was a little sad to see her go.

Carol, a friend for only a day, but a friend nonetheless. Once again, I thought, I might be alone on this trip but I'm certainly not lonely. There are down-to-earth, kind, accepting people everywhere, even in the middle of Africa, and I've been lucky enough to meet them.

Africa! I was heading still farther into Africa. This thought held me captive.

Nature. . . in its many forms,
arouses the senses . . .stimulates the soul,
brings peace to the heart.

11

The Zambezi Lodge

The sunset I saw from the bus that night was as pretty as any postcard you'll ever find. These kinds of trees and ponds I had only seen in pictures, yet now they were so real that I expected to see a hippo come up out of the water. I had seen the giant sandcastle hills made by the ants, and the strange trees and bushes of the Namibian desert, but this was the Africa I had come for.

Early in the morning just before the sun was up I started to see small huts gathered in small clusters each time the trees would clear. There were dirt roads leading out to ponds and an occasional community well. It had rained most of the night so there was a fine mist, almost like fog, hanging close to the ground.

Women had their dishes on their heads returning home from washing them. Some were carrying big vases on their heads filled with enough water for their families for a day.

Many had little children, either babies on their backs or little toddlers walking close on their mothers' heels.

By now the paved road had ended and we were traveling on a dirt road. Construction for a new road was underway, causing people to come out and watch with enthusiasm. All the women wore wraparound dresses and the men had very old, torn cotton pants and shirts. Each time the bus passed these people got all excited and waved big waves to the bus. It was funny because the bus had those dark windows, so even if you wanted to wave back they couldn't see you.

Everything was so green. It looked like wherever someone got an idea to throw out some corn seeds, it just started to grow: no rows, no organized vegetable gardens, just patches scattered here and there, anywhere they had cleared a little space in the trees and the bush.

I began to study the huts. Some were large with no windows, others were small with a few windows. Each was built with sticks for walls and long grass tied together in neat bundles for the roofs. Sometimes there would be three or four huts together, sometimes just one. They looked so tidy. Some had fences made out of sticks around them. Others were set in clearings obviously kept clear somehow from intruding weeds and vegetation.

Many had little pens made out of twisted dead shrubs for their chickens, or even homemade corrals also constructed out of dead sticks and shrubs for their cows. Goats were here and there just wandering on their own.

Once when the bus got stuck in a deep mud puddle, I stuck my head out the window. That sweet scent was the final sensation it took to bring my imagination to life. Now I could see a little girl running back into the bush, hollering at Tawanda to wait up. She was skinny and was wearing a beautiful brown and red colored wrap. In her hand she carried a basket. I wanted to run with her to see what she was up to. But no sooner had I seen her than she disappeared into the trees. I couldn't let her go that soon. I ran in after her and now I could see what was going on. They were throwing stones at a mongoose that had broken their treasured eggs. Wynoma yelled at Tawanda, "He's coming your direction! Quick get him."

Tawanda made a plunge at the mongoose, and this time I could see what all the commotion was about: it was a long squirrel-looking creature with a face kind of like a beaver's except its fur was thick and grey. It was quick, so quick I only caught a glimpse, but now I could see Wynoma with tears in her eyes dumping tiny, broken, speckled eggshells out of her basket. Tawanda came running back. He looked at Wynoma then at the broken eggs. Then, just as he was bending down, . . . our nice attendant came around and asked if me if I wanted coffee. Startled and a bit angry at having my great imaginary adventure interrupted, it was all I could do to just smile and say, "No, thank you."

I wanted to get back to my thoughts, but Wynoma and Tawanda were gone. I put the window back up. Now the bus had got out of the mud puddle and was heading back down the road. Without the fresh vegetation smell and the feel of the damp air on my face the jungle scenes were gone; now it was thoughts as usual. This time I remembered asking Tansy what kind of food she ate. She said maize, maize, maize, and meat, meat, meat. I couldn't help thinking these people looked better off than the people in the townships. This beauty which surrounds them must fill them with more pleasure than the dirty, trashy, confined living conditions in the city.

I thought about the family in the city sitting there relying on selling their wood carvings for a meal. It must be so discouraging to pack up all those huge heavy things into their shopping carts and make several trips home just to start all over again the next day. Wouldn't you begin to grow more and more angry each day as people who seemed rich to you just passed you by like you didn't even exist?

Tansy told me over and over again why they leave their little homes in the bush, "They hear a man can become rich in the big city and never have to work another day in his life. So they pack up some food and with only the shirt on their backs they start to walk and walk and walk. Hmm, this is taking longer than I thought. With his food running out, he grows desperate. He gets to the city. He has no food, no money, no education, destitute.

"Now he must search the trash cans just to stay alive, he can't even get enough food stored up to get back and he falls into the hands of the township. There he struggles just like the rest to get a job, start a life."

So goes one of the stories of the townships.

I was looking at these beautiful surroundings and now I could see why Tansy and Nkosi missed their home in this kind of world and wanted to return so badly. I can also see why her friend's husband left Cape Town to return to Zambia's grief-stricken soil in search of a job---any job---just to be able to stay there and live.

As soon as we crossed over the border into Botswana, someone on the bus said real loudly, "Now we're gonna see some elephants."

Everything was becoming even more lush and mysterious. There were trees as big around at the base as a car; they were the giant baobab trees. This is exactly how I had pictured Africa to be. Tarzan himself would be the only thing that could have made it more complete. I lived for those Tarzan movies when I was a girl.

Almost everyone on the bus was up now and watching out of every window for the elephants. It was funny that even these people who had seen elephants a hundred times were still in awe of the big creatures. Someone shouted, "There's one!"

It was! Two of them actually, just eating at the side of the road. As we passed they took very little notice of us. One slowly turned around and then moseyed back into the bushes. I wished I could have stayed in this setting longer.

Now came the border of Zimbabwe. Our bus had a man attendant, well actually just a boy. He had been so friendly, I really liked him. He seemed to enjoy his job of checking out our passports, serving us hard biscuits, tea and coffee day and night. One time I asked him if he had any water. He reached down, dumped out his melted ice water from the cooler in which he kept drinks you could purchase, poured it into a cup, and handed it to me.

"Ice water, madam, at your service."

I drank it. I was too cheap to buy a drink, and the water at the bathroom stops was a sick brown color.

Now before the trip started the bus driver had asked me if I had enough money to get into Zimbabwe, and I assured him that I had money. At the border the official said, "You must pay one hundred and sixty rands to get in."

I looked in my wallet and saw that I had a one hundred-rand bill and a twenty-dollar bill from America. I offered him what I had.

He snapped, "No, you can't mix currencies."

An American twenty-dollar bill was worth about one hundred and twenty rands. He was being difficult, so I went back to the bus and dug in the bottom of my bag and got out my reserve purse. I took out two one hundred- rand bills, went back in, and handed them to him. The nice boy who was my attendant was really trying to help me. But now the man said he couldn't make change.

The boy piped in, "Come on." He had been standing next to me the whole time and by now even he was getting perturbed. The border guard kept letting other people in front of me and acted really busy. One lady in front of me paid him in Namibian money; I watched him put it in his drawer.

He then said, "Go ask the people on your bus for change." So I gave my two one hundred-rand bills to the boy, and he ran back to the bus to ask everyone if they could help out this poor American. The bus driver gave him two fifties for one of the hundreds. He came running back in and handed the man the two bills.

He objected saying, "No, not close enough."

By now the boy and I were both getting really frustrated. Luckily, I had learned the hard way in Namibia that Namibian money was worth the same as rands.

So I said, "Just give me my change in Namibian dollars. I know you have some, I just saw that lady pay you in Namibian money."

There was a long pause. He said something to his buddy in some African language. Another long pause. Then he motioned something to a boy who was standing at the back and he went in another room and came out with two twenty-rands, my change! He had the change all along. Another attempt to outsmart the stupid Americans.

Driving into Zimbabwe, I don't know how it was possible but the vegetation became even more dense. Looking on the map back at home, I saw this was the only part of central Africa that was considered a rain forest, partly due to the Falls and partly because of the size of the Zambezi River. The elevation begins to drop, thus creating a tropical environment. It began to rain but it was still quite warm. It was the first time I had been in such humid conditions. No wonder the mosquitoes were so bad.

Except for an occasional stop to gas up, this bus made no stops. When it did stop, the bathrooms, or what they called bathrooms, were sometimes just a hole in the ground with no seats, and a tiny sink where brown water came out. The bathrooms and the mosquitoes made you want to stay on the bus. But it was always a toss-up which was worse, the bathroom on the bus or the one at the bus stops. The bus had a tiny little three-foot by three-foot cubicle, which tons of stinky travelers filled up in no time.

It was about one in the afternoon when we reached Victoria Falls. The first thing I noticed was how small the town was, but it looked inviting. The bus was supposed to drop me off at the post office. There was one little main street with a few shops and a few cafes, one major bank, and a railroad track. There were a few people and maybe three taxis (you can't tell the taxis from any other cars) waiting at the post office when our bus arrived. A safari- looking man came right up to me with a sign that read, "I'm looking for Mr. Rogers."

How embarrassing! I was certainly not Mister Rogers but since there were only five people getting off the bus, I figured the sign must be for me. I told him I was Mrs. Rogers and he could put down that silly sign. As if he couldn't just ask the five people getting off the bus if they were Mr. Rogers. He had been sent by Tansy's friend at the embassy to take me to the Zambezi Lodge. He was so friendly and talkative, but I was exhausted; I didn't feel like talking. All I wanted to do was go to my room and sleep. Anyone who has ever tried to sleep on a bus knows what I mean. When I arrived at the Zambezi Lodge it was like nothing I had ever seen before. It was nestled back in the thick jungle with one small, and two giant, thatched-roof huts.

In the small hut---the office---sat an older white woman behind a desk. (It occurs to me as I write this, that it is strange that I should need to mention that she is white. But a white person was now the exception in the places I was in.) She was apparently the owner. After getting me signed in, she asked what I would be doing for supper. At this point I felt as if I were in a daze. I told her, "Nothing, all I want to do is sleep."

She was shocked that I had spent three days on the bus. Her guests usually fly in. She motioned to a man to get my bags and show me to my room. Then she added, "I hope you won't be needing anything more. I leave here at five, but the night watchmen will be here."

"Thank you."

As I walked to my room I tried hard to take it all in. I could tell she had a bunch of black men who worked for her. They all stared at me as I went to my room. The one who took my bags must have had the most authority as he was the only one who spoke to me.

As I followed him down a little winding path through the trees, I noticed I had a small crystal-clear pool right outside my room. Many of the plants that were growing all around me I recognized as houseplants back home. My room was inside the first large hut. The first thing I noticed inside was the smell. It was a musty, hot grass mixed with dirt, kind of earthy smell, yet it was cool as a cave inside. In the first room were all kinds of stuffed, big-game, animals: heads, horns, even big elephant feet and the weapons you'd use to kill them. We walked past a tearoom, a small kitchen, and a big dining-room table on our way to the hall. Down the hall were three rooms, each one had two beds and a bath.

It was so quiet. I hadn't seen anyone else, but I was too tired to care. Inside my room I noticed the ceiling was very high. There was a little ledge over my bathroom and on it stood an old hot-water heater. I remember thinking how strange to have that hot-water heater with open flames underneath sitting right next to the dry grass thatched roof. It looked very old, so I decided that since it had not started a fire yet, I would be safe for a few more days. In the bathroom was a little sign that read, "Although we are located by one of the world's largest rivers, we do experience water shortages. We apologize if you should find that we are out of water. The management."

Panic-stricken, I tried the water. "Yes! Water!" It was brown water, but a hot brown bath ain't too bad after three days on a bus. The room had a little table and even a little refrigerator. A good thing since with the size of the huge beetles and cockroaches I had seen, it wouldn't have taken them very long to eat all your food.

It was so hot and humid that I had to leave the windows open. None of the windows had screens, but at least the bed had a mosquito net. There were no bars on the windows either. My bed was even with the window at ground level, and that made me a bit nervous. The thought had crossed my mind that someone could just crawl into my room, but I was too tired to worry about that. I got myself organized, took a bath, sprayed on tons of mosquito repellent, tried to figure out the mosquito net, and went to bed. I had spent at least three nights with little or no sleep and now I felt it. I fell into a complete and totally exhausted sleep as soon as my head hit the pillow. I knew I had entered into a whole new world. . . . Tomorrow I would appreciate it.

Languages may change,
and customs seem strange,
yet nature will remain constant,
and will invite all to partake.

12

"The Seeing Side"

I have always been fond of early-morning sounds. It's that transitional time between total darkness and the infusion of light, and total silence and the intrusion of sound. At home in summer it starts around four A.M. Even though nature is waking up to a new day, it has a quiet way of introducing itself, respecting all who may still be asleep.

Often, I'll lie in my bed drifting in and out of sleep while the songs of the birds soothe my soul. Each bird has its own unique style. They are all so different, and yet if anyone asked, "Which is your favorite?" I couldn't answer. I heard the same sounds each dawn for many years.

This was one of those mornings when you wake up and briefly wonder where you are while your mind gets oriented. I was awakened by sounds so unfamiliar to me that I couldn't tell if they were exotic birds or maybe tropical tree frogs. I had heard a similar sound once when my son's tiny tree frogs in his terrarium decided to sing. They have more like a song than a croak. It took us all by surprise. This morning it took me a long time to figure out where I was. All I did know was that I was very far from home and in the middle of either a dream or some strange reality.

I kept wishing my friends from home could experience this. I knew I would never be able to describe it to them. Even the smells were new to me. I didn't know if it was the thick trees outside or the thatched roof on the inside, but something made it seem so quiet. Was I the only one here?

By now I remembered breakfast and I was so hungry. I got dressed, put more mosquito repellent on, and went exploring. Straight down the hall was the dining-room table set for breakfast. Mapenzi, the man who carried my bags last evening, was here to welcome me again. "Good morning. Did you sleep well?"

"Oh, yes, thank you."

"Would you like coffee or tea?"

I had never met people who drank so much coffee and tea. Seems they were asking you every two hours on the bus.

"Will you have coffee or tea?" he asked again.

"No, thank you, but I'm starving for real food. What's for breakfast?"

"What do you want? We have cereal and milk, we have all very much good food the cook has cooked for you. How do you like your eggs?"

His English was broken but easy to understand. I told him it all looked good to me. Then the cook came out and asked how I would like my eggs. I answered, "I'll have them scrambled. Do you have any yogurt?"

Another man came out and asked if he could do any laundry for me. They were all so kind and pleasant to me, each one trying to outdo the other. I wasn't used to being pampered quite like this. The owner of the lodge arrived around nine. These nice men ran the place for her. She had one to do the laundry, one to do the cleaning, one to cook, one to manage, and a couple of guys that seemed as if their job was to just hang around.

A couple came and sat down. They were from England but were checking out that morning. They must have been down the other hall, as I hadn't heard anyone else. Then another fellow came and sat down. He was also from England and was checking out too. I had hoped I would meet someone at the lodge to spend my days with. Well, I guess I was on my own today.

The British couple and the British man excused themselves, so I was alone to finish my breakfast. It seemed that these black men were all a bit curious to see this white woman from America. They would try to think up reasons to be in and around the breakfast table. One started dusting, another one kept coming in and out to check the food, while Mapenzi just stood there looking important.

As I sat finishing my breakfast, I asked if they would like to hear a story about my home. That broke the ice. They each got a big smile and immediately gathered around the table as I took out my pictures.

"It is so nice," one man said as he pointed to my flowers.

One of my flower beds sits up against our dog pen. One man asked, "Are these your dogs?"

That triggered an idea in me. I would tell them about our dogs.

"Yes, these are my dogs, Patch and Sipsy. They are hunting dogs called pointers because they have a inborn instinct to point. Small birds such as pheasants and chuckars hide in the bushes, and the only way a hunter can find these hidden birds is by using hunting dogs. You've probably heard of hunting dogs but I am going to tell you about mine. Patch has big white and brown spots all over him, but Sipsy is brown all over. Now a good hunting dog is hard to come by. What they should do is run back and forth through the fields searching for birds. But they are not searching as a man searches; they are sniffing the air constantly. They don't have to see the bird, they just catch the scent. As they run back and forth through a field they can cover much more ground than a man ever could. There they are, running full force, when all of the sudden they stop right dead in their tracks, frozen in place. They don't see a bird but they smell one very close by. They stand there frozen like a statue, and wait for the hunter. This is called holding point."

By this time more men had joined in listening and they were wide-eyed and intense as I continued.

"Now the hunter comes up and walks ahead of the dogs where they are pointing. Voila! the bird flies out and the hunter shoots. For many dogs the desire to go in and get that bird surpasses the discipline needed for him to stand and wait for his master. It is a thing of beauty to see one that has the instinct and desire do his work. If it's not a good dog, the dog chases in after the bird and scares it up before the hunter has a chance to get there. Sipsy is not as good as Patch, she loses interest in pointing, so she sometimes rushes in too soon and scares the birds away. Not Patch, he holds point for a long time. Once he was holding point, and we kicked and stomped in the bushes, but no bird. We kicked again, no bird. Finally we said, 'Come on, Patch, there's no bird in there,' and we walked away.

"Patch would not come but remained on point. As we walked farther away, he rushed in, out flew a bird. He knew it was there, but we didn't believe him. We always trusted him after that."

By now all the men were standing around listening, so I started in again.

128

"I have two favorite times of year to go walking with my dogs. One is late September. Back home, September is a golden month. The fields have all been baked from the summer sun. The air has taken on a hint of the cooler months to come. The temperature is perfect, especially in the evenings. Now if your timing is just right, you'll catch the sun right as it dips below the horizon and for the next few moments the most vivid reds, yellows, and oranges all take on a golden luster. All of your surroundings are golden. But it only lasts a few moments, and very few people ever see the magic.

"My other favorite time to take the dogs out is early on a winter morning, after it has snowed all night. When we get out early, before the sun comes up, everything is pure white. The earth has a white blanket covering it. The air is crisp and cold so you can see the dogs' breath as they run ahead. The new white blanket has muffled the sounds, just the same as when you get down under a pile of covers. All is quiet. The only sound is the breathing of the dogs. It feels almost as if you are losing your hearing. By taking away one sense, the others seem magnified. You'll see ice crystals floating in the frozen air, tree limbs touching the ground heavy with the weight of snow, and each slender stem on every bush is a shimmering white. The whole world sparkles with the rising of the sun."

I was finding out that nature is a universal language. If I tried to explain an escalator in a department store in the mall, a microwave, or a computer, they just couldn't imagine it. But everyone has seen the sun rise, touched a tree, or listened to a bird sing.

This little silk pouch my daughter had made contained my favorite pictures. I had many pictures of my flower gardens, our favorite mountain to climb covered in wild flowers, and a winter scene with my home covered in snow. Everyone I had met without exception had loved my pictures. It was my way of bringing a small piece of my world to them.

We had talked almost an hour when I remembered I had signed up for a tour that morning. I thanked my more-than-cordial listeners, and hurried to my room to get my things together for the day.

As I entered the office, the same women I had met the day before informed me that my tour was running a bit late. While I stood in the driveway, Mapenzi stood waiting with me. He was always there to help,

"Madam, your ride is here. Madam, your breakfast is ready. Madam, your ride will be late, can I get you something?"

I spent much of my time talking to him. I asked him how far it was to town; I didn't mind walking. Did he think I could walk to town. He said, "Oh, yes, it is not far to town." He walked it all the time.

At last my ride pulled up. The driver was a black man. A black woman sat next to him; they were together. I wondered who else was going on this tour; the rest of the van was empty. Well, it looked like I was their only passenger. I was off to the craft village. I thanked Mapenzi and said my goodbye. Obviously this must be where you go to buy crafts, right? That's what I thought too. But wrong, the van took me to an actual true-to-life African village. When I got out of the van, they asked when they should pick me up. I replied, "I don't know. I would like to take some time. Come back and get me in four hours."

They looked surprised but agreed.

In the village I had a real fun tour guide. He explained everything to me, and I asked a lot of questions. In the village they had separate huts; some were used for cooking and others for sleeping. He showed me all the tools they made. They even made things out of metal without electricity. It was fascinating. I took plenty of pictures, many with my cute tour guide in them.

He was the first of many to ask me to send him his pictures. He got out a piece of paper and wrote down his address. My tour was finished, so I asked my guide how to get to the Falls. He told me to walk the dirt road back to town, turn left, and I would be headed to the Falls.

As I entered town, I was suddenly bombarded by about twenty young men who all asked me at once, "Madam, please, see this beautiful wood hippo. Madam, please, see this beautiful wood elephant. Madam, it would be so nice on your table."

They were beautiful too. But Tansy had told me to wait.

"Be sure and buy your souvenirs in Zambia; they are so poor you can buy things very cheap."

These boys were so persistent though. I asked how much.

"For you, Madam, one hundred and fifty zims."

Oh, I hadn't thought about Zimbabwe dollars yet. I only had rands. In fact, I had no idea what the exchange rate was. I did have quite a few coins, American and South African. I figured when I felt compelled to give I could give away my coins. They couldn't take coins. The banks in town didn't want to take the time to figure out the exchange rate on coins so they simply said no coins. So now what good were all these coins I had saved up for the cause?

I told them I had just arrived and I needed to go to a bank; but I had four daughters at home, if they could find me necklaces.

"Necklaces?"

I pointed to my neck and then to theirs.

"Only tiny things. I can't take anything home that is too heavy."

"But this is not too heavy, see."

"I can't take these things on the bus with me."

131

After plenty of refusing and sticking to my story, they backed off.

"What time will you be back here?"

"Two hours. If you'll have some necklaces ready for me then we'll talk."

I started walking toward the Falls. Then one of them said, "But madam, please, take my picture and send it to me."

"All right." I had him write down his name and address on my magazine.

Now I was finally off to see the Falls. It was quite a walk. People were selling fruit and tomatoes all along the road. My daughter Jenny, an aspiring artist at Utah State University, asked me to get pictures of the children, lots of pictures of children. Every time I stopped to take a picture of tiny children they were afraid of me, so they would run back to their mommas, or they would start to cry.

I finally arrived at the gate to the Falls. Some boys were selling bottled water and pop. When one approached me I had to say, "I'm sorry I have no zims."

He said, "No problem. They have change over there," pointing to a man sitting at a desk who was selling pamphlets about the Falls.

Now this persistent boy who was selling the water made sure I knew his name. "When you come back you ask for Innocent, yes? Remember Innocent."

I went over to see the pamphlets. They were nice, only thirty rands. I handed him fifty rands, and he gave me change in zims.

Since there was a charge to get into the park to see the Falls, I decided to wait and go the next day as I had already paid for the tour.

I walked back across the street and there was Innocent waiting for me. I asked, "Okay, how much for the water?"

He answered, "One hundred and fifty zims."

I laughed, "No way! I only have fifty zims. How about some change?"

"No, madam. They don't take those coins around here."

Well, I had some Juicy Fruit gum so I gave him the gum and fifty zims. Not only was he thrilled about the gum but he made out like a bandit on the water.

Walking back I decided to go down by the river. As I was walking I saw two white girls ahead of me. They were backpackers from Germany. They spoke a little English, so I walked with them. We had only gone a little ways when a policeman stopped us.

"You girls should not walk down to the river alone; two girls were attacked right here only two days ago."

"Right on this trail?"

"Yes, right on this trail."

Then one girl said, "Well, if you walk with us, we won't be alone, will we?"

Once again I had a tour guide. He was very nice. He told us about the trees, the flowers, and even the crocodiles in the river, how they fished on the river, the Falls in the rainy seasons versus the Falls in the dry season. He even took us to the "big tree," which is very famous because that's where they finally found Dr Livingstone. Thus was heard the famous quotation, "Dr. Livingstone, I presume?"

I took pictures of the river, the lush vegetation, and the "big tree," guessed to be over fifteen hundred years old. It had a tiny chain-link fence around it to keep vandals out. Yeah, right. There were a few names carved in it. I noticed that the backpacker girls weren't taking pictures; I guess it's just one more thing to carry.

Now the policeman had to say goodbye. "This is as far as my watch goes."

I took his picture, something that everyone around there thinks is such an honor. We thanked him and walked up the dirt road following his directions. We walked for quite some time when I just had to ask, "Are you sure this is the way to town because my ride will be there to pick me up in two hours."

One gal answered, "I don't know, but it looks like it to me."

Up ahead was a little café, so we went in to get a cola. We sat down in this quaint little place, and I found myself saying for the umpteenth time, "Well, you've heard of California, right."

"Yes."

"Utah, is kind of by California."

"Oh, okay."

I ordered an orange Fanta, which turned out to be a lemonade. I was getting used to surprises by now; I just grinned and drank it. Then I asked the man how much for a bottled water.

"About twenty-four zims."

I just smiled.

Walking back I had forgotten all about my favorite boys and the wood carvings. Well, they certainly had not forgotten about me. They all came running up when they saw me. Every one of them had necklaces, bracelets, and all kinds of small trinkets. I didn't know who to talk to first. Then I remembered I had no zims. I told them to give me a half-hour while I went to the bank.

I walked down the only street in town to what I thought was a bank. It turned out to be more like a pawnshop. I handed him my last twenty dollar-bill from the States.

One of our dollars was worth thirty-eight zims. When he counted the money back to me, it looked like fake money. I said, "Are you sure this is real money?"

He replied, somewhat offended, "Oh, yes, madam, you buy from me, not the man on the street."

Yeah, right. His joint looked like the man on the street.

Then as I walked back to meet the boys, the men on the street approached me. "Madam, we give you good deal: thirty-eight zims for one American dollar."

"Sorry, I already bought from over there." And I was glad I did; these guys had counterfeit money for sure.

As I walked up, all the boys came running. I don't know where they got them all, but I had never seen so many necklaces. Some were carved from rock, some were carved from wood, some even had basket-woven bracelets.

"Whoa, wait a minute. I can't possibly buy all of these."

"But, madam," one boy was saying, "you promised me. See, four necklaces for your daughters, remember?"

I did remember him, so I agreed; I had promised him.

"But, madam, you see how nice little rhinos are."

"But, madam, see rock elephants."

"Madam, bracelets, they don't weigh."

I wanted to buy from them all; they were all so cute.

"Okay, I'll get one of yours, one of yours, three of yours, four of yours," until my money ran out. Even though my van had to wait a bit for me, he had enjoyed watching the spectacle. He was laughing when I got back to the van.

I decided after that I should avoid town, being by myself and being the sucker that I am. I didn't want to be bombarded by this kind of thing again.

On my ride back to the Lodge the man in the van asked if I would like to go on a sunset cruise to see the Zambezi River. I told him I was a little short on cash, but he assured me it was only six hundred zims or about eighteen American dollars. I couldn't resist.

Back at the lodge things were quiet. I wanted to go for a swim but when I began I noticed the men trying to make up jobs to do around the pool. I started feeling a little uneasy. Should I let thoughts like these ruin my trip, or not. I guess I did. I got out of the pool and went to my room where I would be "safe."

I had planned to eat one night at a real restaurant. I picked the Boma because it had native dancing for entertainment. When I got ready to go, I asked the night watchman to call me a taxi. While we were waiting for it to come we visited. This man was young, only about twenty. The other night watchman was old and didn't speak any English. The older man was cooking dinner for the both of them on a tiny open fire outside. I was asking the young man where he was from. He said, "My family lives about five hours from here in the bush. They don't even know this place."

He said he had a girlfriend that he sees every April when he gets off for a month.

"Why doesn't she come see you?" I asked.

"She has no way of making money so she has never been on a bus."

Our conversation was cut short by the arrival of my taxi. "Oops, got to go. See you later." I was off to the Boma.

My taxi driver was also very young. Maybe because most young people can speak English they have the jobs that deal directly with the tourists. Any young person who has been to primary school in Africa has been taught English. He asked me the usual questions: where I was from and how long I was staying.

I explained to him where Utah was in the United States. Then, just to get it off my mind, I explained to him that the owner of the Lodge told me the taxi ride would cost ten rands or fifty zims. I did not carry extra money. He said, "Well, it is a little more than that because this is so far away, but we will work something out."

I asked if he would come back and get me or if he wanted to wait for me. He said he would come back for me. I took his picture, and he gave me his address.

"THE SEEING SIDE"

The Boma was indescribable. It was inside a huge grass hut with trees growing right up the middle of the restaurant. There were three big open barbecue pits and only lanterns for light. They were so friendly; I wondered if everyone got this kind of treatment or if they were going all out because I was alone. First they washed my hands, then they begged me to taste their own African beer, the smell of which alone could have killed you off.

This and the African village were run totally by the black African natives, so the buildings and the food were totally authentic to their home, Zimbabwe. Their main object was to make you have an African experience, which you did. Crocodile tail, ostrich kabobs, warthog steaks, water buffalo stew, and, of course, caterpillars. It was all buffet-style, so you could taste as many different items as your stomach could stand. To top it all off you could have the medicine man read your fortune by tossing the bones.

I had a feeling that although it was run by blacks, all the forms of entertainment for the tourists were owned by the whites. It was all the stuff we would expect on a vacation. From bungee-jumping off the world's highest bridge at sixty U.S. dollars a shot to staying in the Victoria Falls Hotel at two hundred U.S. dollars a night. We who are civilized can always think of a way to make money, right? It just seems that the native people whose land this really is should get back more in return.

When I got back to the lodge, James, my driver, and I settled up with some rands and some zims. The taxi drivers seemed real happy and they loved to talk to you. I was feeling pretty good about the world after talking with him.

It was mysteriously dark and quiet at the Lodge. It wasn't the first time I wished someone else was staying here, but I could do nothing about that.

When I got back in my room the first thing I did was open the closet to check on my real purse. It had a separate lock and the owner assured me my things would be safe. When I opened it up the first thing I noticed was that the zipper on my purse had been broken. I wrestled with myself as to whether or not it had been broken before and I just hadn't noticed it. I hurriedly dumped the contents out on my bed. My passport was there, both my charge cards were there, my pictures, my pen and papers, even my money was there, or was it? I suspected that some money was missing. I was puzzled but glad that they had not taken all my money.

I began to wonder about the whole thing. Either someone was right in the middle of stealing from me when they heard me coming so they broke my zipper in their haste to get out of there, or maybe they had every intention of stealing everything, then seeing the contents of my purse (you can tell a lot about a woman by the contents of her purse), changed their mind. I had beautiful pictures of flowers, a family, and a card that a dear friend had given me before I left home. It had a little angel pinned on the card and it read something like this: "Here is a little guardian angel. It has been blessed with a prayer for you the traveler. May you be protected and loved on your journey."

Could this be enough to make them change their mind? I guess I will never know. There were only two people there and I suspected it was one of them, either the night watchman or the young boy. I was sorry to think it was the boy. He needed this job. How could I tell on him? Maybe it was someone I hadn't even suspected?

Then my worries changed course. Now it wasn't the money at all that had me worried, it was the thought that someone had a key to my room.

This was the first time I was afraid to be alone. How could I have been so stupid? There was no one around, not even within screaming distance. I couldn't get to a phone and even if I could, who would I call? I had to get hold of myself; my mind was running away with me. As scared as I was, as alone as I was, I don't ever remember needing my prayers to reach to heaven more.

For a few moments I lay in bed tossing and turning. Then came the miracle I had prayed for: a peaceful feeling came over me and I was able to sleep contentedly all that night.

The next morning the table was set as usual with enough place mats and dishes for about ten people. I got up and said to the cleaning man, "You don't need to clean my room today; just wash these towels and this pillowcase, okay?"

This morning everyone became a suspect. When he smiled shyly and answered, "Yes, madam," I thought, "No, it couldn't be him."

Mapenzi was there to greet me. He asked, "How was your dinner? Where are you going today?"

"To see the Falls."

"Are you taking a guided tour to see the Falls?"

"Yes, they will be here at ten."

"Oh, you'll like that."

"Mapenzi, I am having a hard time finding pictures of children to take for my daughter. Maybe you can help."

"There are many children at the compound. That's where I live, I will take you there."

"Do *you* have children? How far is it?"

"Oh, yes, madam, my wife and I have many children. It is not far, we can walk to it after I get off work today."

"Okay! What time do you get off work?"

"Three o'clock."

"It's a date."

Now I was sure it wasn't him; he was a family man.

Just then a couple came in the room. "Are we expecting more guests?" they commented.

"No," I said, "this is how it always looks in the morning, I even thought I was the only one here."

"We got in last night, but we must be on opposite ends of the huts because we thought we were the only ones here. It was so quiet last night."

They were from Germany. The woman spoke better English than the man. I told them I was going to see the Falls in about an hour and that they were welcome to come along with me. They wondered if my tour could fit them in at the last minute like this. I assured them I had my own tour guide and I was sure he wouldn't mind. More money for him, right?

As we waved goodbye, Mapenzi said, "You won't forget what we had talked about, will you, Madam Rogers?"

"Well, if I had that much money, I'd be happy too!"

13

Teiso's Taxi

It was just as I had thought when my tour guide pulled up. I said, "Where is everyone else? I thought this was a tour."

"Madam, you are the tour."

I asked if some friends I met that morning could come along.

"Of course, tell them to get in."

So we all got in, and I was off to see what I had come all these many miles to see. Isaac, the driver, was such a pleasant guy; hadn't all the guys been pleasant? I began to wonder if this was just a coincidence. I also noticed that many of these fellows had biblical names. Those first missionaries must have made quite an impression.

Isaac was getting out of the car when he turned back around and pulled an umbrella out of his front seat. That's strange, I thought, today is nice and sunny.

"Hey, Isaac, you expecting rain?"

He just smiled.

We began our tour of the Falls in a large open field. Isaac led us down a path thick with vegetation on each side. After climbing down some steps, half-hidden because of all the undergrowth, we began to hear the Falls. The trees were so dense that you couldn't see anything, you just started to hear this sound. It started to get louder and louder until now it was so loud that I knew why the policeman said the natives call these Falls, "the smoke that thunders."

Then in a clearing we stood on an overhang and saw the Falls for the first time. Unbelievable. The mist was so thick and rose so high; this was the cloud the natives were talking about. The vegetation, the water, the land all around, were all virtually untouched, left totally preserved, just the way the first explorer saw it.

As the water falls over the gorge it drops so far that its splash creates water droplets the size of rain, thus creating the rain forest around it. It constantly rains so we were soaked in no time, but not Isaac. It was a warm rain, so we didn't mind. I couldn't get the length of the Falls down in my mind because they kept saying it was so many kilometers. That's when Isaac told me they were at one point three miles long. Wow!

He told us that during the dry season the water in the river goes down and the Falls run shorter. But this was their rainy season and the Falls reached all the way. The beauty was indescribable; a picture can't do it justice. It's the mist, the roar, the multicolored ribbons of water, the ferns, the rainbows, the river, and the cool breeze all combined that make it so breathtaking. It's one of the seven wonders of the world, and I could see why.

I had seen waterfalls before---at Yellowstone, Mesa, and Niagara--- but this had to be God's greatest masterpiece in the creation of water spectaculars! My first glimpse of the Falls had not overwhelmed me; it wasn't until we had walked the full length of the vista and we turned around to look back to see the Falls in their entirety that the full impact of the wonder hit me; I was brought to tears. The thought came to me that God had created this just for us!

We walked the whole mile and a half until we reached the bridge that joins the two countries, Zimbabwe and Zambia. Now I got my first sight of Zambia, a country that until now I only knew with words. I couldn't wait to go there. Nkosi had told me that the Falls are better from the Zambian side, the "feeling side." The river turned under the bridge and continued to flow down the bottom of the gorge. Standing on the bridge your eyes could follow the river and the gorge until they met the horizon and dropped out of sight.

I couldn't get enough. I didn't want to leave knowing I would never be back, but it's one of those things you can't take with you, and no one will ever know what you're talking about unless they see it for themselves. For a few moments I was speechless to think that I was so fortunate.

I turned to Isaac and said, "You are so lucky to have a job like this; I wonder if you know just how lucky. To see this beauty everyday, to see peoples' reactions, it has got to be good for your soul. There are so many people caught in the rat race, working hard at a job they hate."

He just smiled. How could he even begin to know what I was talking about?

At the end of a wonderful experience, I couldn't stop thanking Isaac enough as he drove me back to the Lodge. I think he must have been relieved to see me go.

Back at the Lodge, Mapenzi stood there, smiling, patiently waiting for me. I had almost forgotten about our agreement. It was three o'clock and obviously he hadn't.

The lady who owned the Lodge happened to see me leaving with Mapenzi. She yelled out the window, "Where are you going?"

"To the compound to take pictures of the children."

"Come here a minute, I need to talk to you."

I walked into the office, and she continued, "Do you know how far that is?"

I think she thought that if I knew, it would change my mind, and she was looking for something to change my mind. She looked so concerned.

"I don't mind. I like to walk." I tried to alleviate her concern.

"Well, sit down. I am going to call you a taxi."

I smiled to myself. Whatever she wanted I was willing to go along with, as long as she didn't ruin our plans. While we waited for a taxi, I explained about my daughter being an artist and wanting me to take pictures of the children for her.

When the taxi finally arrived, I heard her tell the driver, "Whatever you do, don't let this woman out of your sight."

I took ten packs of Juicy Fruit gum for the children, ten rands for the cab, and my camera. We were off.

I don't know what I was expecting the compound to be but I was not thinking it was this. Now I was seeing the heart of my Africa trip. This is where the men live who cooked for me, cleaned for me, drove for me, and made sure my trip was comfortable. This is home for them. This was the part of Africa most people don't see, tucked away, back behind the trees, far from where the rich tourists stay. This is real life for these people. When we go out on our animal safaris, our guided tours, and stay in our fancy hotels, we never think about where our cute, friendly guide lives. It broke my heart.

Mapenzi didn't bring me here for pity; he didn't want my sympathy, he wanted my friendship. So that is exactly what I gave. I acted like it didn't even faze me. They opened up their shabby little homes to me. With nothing but a tree stump for me to sit on, Mapenzi introduced me to his family, then the neighbors, and more neighbors, and more neighbors. I was laughing with them, taking their pictures, and telling them about my daughter who paints. "If she paints your picture I may send one to you." They all believed I would too.

My taxi driver, Teiso, ended up being the most helpful and most friendly of all. He would talk to the children in their language, telling them not to be afraid of this strange white lady. I created quite a stir, and they all wanted to know what I was up to.

Each person wanted us to send them their pictures. So Teiso and I started making a list and I said it was up to him to see that each person got them. Then we started to joke about becoming famous with our pictures. We laughed about getting rich off National Geographic when they offer to buy our pictures. I enjoyed myself so much I asked him to come and get me the next day and we would come here again and take more pictures.

I didn't want him to think I was offended or afraid to see these dirty little shacks where the clothes hanging on the children looked more like rags than clothes. He might not enjoy my company if he thought these things bothered me. I was actually bothered very little by those things, but I was attracted and pulled into the warmth and friendship of the people.

That night I had so much to think about I completely forgot about being afraid. If there were jobs only for the men (the men held all the jobs and not enough jobs at that), then where were all these kids going to get jobs? The women looked so tired. All they knew was having kids and trying to feed their family. The men come to places like this lodge and know that there's more out there.

There was a subdued, quiet, feeling in the Lodge that night. Everyone had gone home but the night watchmen. I went into the sitting room. It was dark that night, very dark; there was no moon. Now all the animal heads on the walls begin to cast eerie shadows in the room. Lack of light, mixed with the smell of the grass hut, made me feel I was in a place so far from home.

After being alone with my thoughts for quite some time I wanted someone to talk to. I could tell that the watchmen were a little restless tonight. They kept pacing back and forth; maybe they were used to more guests coming and going.

I sat there swatting mosquitoes when Mugunda walked in. He was the young night watchman I had talked to about his home five hours away and his girlfriend. I started talking to him.

"Come sit down and talk to me; it isn't busy tonight."

He started right off by posing a loaded question at me.

"So, where did you go today? Let me guess: a tour of the Falls, bungee-jumping, or did you ride to an animal park?"

No, actually Mapenzi took me to the compound."

He was totally caught off guard by that. Then he just sat there in silence so I continued, "What I really want to know is if the life I saw today is better than in the little villages I saw on my way here. Please, talk to me." After I sprung my question on him, he enlightened me more.

"Life in the village is hard. Many times you have wild animals coming into your home. Sometimes there is drought. Even when the rains do come you have very little to eat. You must work constantly just to stay alive. It seems like all the people do is have babies, babies they can't really afford."

I found myself being caught in a situation for which I had no answers.

I am an eternal optimist. I have always believed that if you want something badly enough you can find a way to get it. I was stumped. Then, as if the conversation did a complete turnaround Mugunda started to let out what I could tell was pent-up anger, "You Americans have one maybe two babies; you have birth control. You do not know what it is like to go to bed hungry. You have nice homes. You have nice schools. You have medicine when you get sick to take away the suffering. My father has fifteen children, I am second to the youngest, and I want to go to school, a university. But all the money I make here goes to my family back home. Then I go to see them once a year. No one in my family knows places like this. They have no money to take a bus to get here. We live in the bush and we have nothing. The rest of my money goes for my own food. Food is expensive here because the tourists can afford it so the storeowner charges what the tourists can afford.

Oh, he really let it all out. In an effort to defend Americans, I said, "I live in a small town in America; we are not all rich. I have five children of my own. I had to save many for years to get enough money to come here. Not all Americans are rich."

Just then I heard myself, and it simply wasn't true! Compared to them we were all rich. I am a person who still believes in America, and that anyone willing to work hard for a better life can get it.

We both sat there in silence. It was true that, compared to them, I felt rich. But I had never considered myself rich before because I knew people who actually were. Million-dollar homes, fancy cars, trips to anywhere in the world---I knew what rich was, right? Rich! Now that all depended on who you are and where you are.

I tried to think of something. Why did the thought come to me right now that this could be the person who had broken into my wallet last night? Was it because I wanted to say I know you took my money so if you'll feel sorry and never steal again things will go better for you? No, I couldn't blame him; his heart was pleading for a way to get to school.

So many thoughts were flowing through my mind. I was thinking, searching. At that moment, I remembered Tansy's mother, Wynoma, and the promise she made. Education was the answer I was looking for. He said it himself: all he wanted was to go to a university. That's the answer.

I asked for his address and said, "I'll see what I can do to help you get to school."

Will wonders never cease? That's all it took. The despair in his eyes turned to a little twinkle. He was so happy that when he ran back to get a piece of paper, I don't think his feet even touched the ground.

I wasn't sure how much I could do but I made myself a promise right then and there that I would do something. It felt real good to know that if I couldn't help them all, I would help just this one. I actually went to bed with a happy heart that night.

Early the next morning at breakfast the German couple told me they had some money stolen from their room the night before. I asked them about what time. They said about five o'clock in the afternoon. Well, at least it was before Mugunda and I had had our talk. I didn't believe that after our talk he would have stolen. They said whoever it was took only fifty dollars out of a huge stack of bills and nothing else. I told them about my break-in too. They wanted to tell the owner. I said, "Oh, but these people need the money; I don't want them to lose their job."

"Right, but the owner needed to know because it was bad for her business." Sadly I agreed.

We told the owner and she agreed that something had to be done, but no one should lose their job. She called the police, but I was gone by the time they came.

When Teiso came to pick me up he was wearing a dress shirt now. I was tickled because I could tell he had dressed up just for me, well okay, for the occasion. Anyway, we drove first to his brother's house. He introduced me to his sister-in-law and we went into her house to get a drink. I had to refuse because I knew I couldn't drink their water, or drink out of their cups. We had a nice visit, but it was a little strange, a little uncomfortable.

Teiso and I had a long talk about the person who was stealing. I said, wanting to show him that I understood their dire circumstances, "At least they only took one bill."

"Yes, madam, but it is wrong to take anything from someone else."

This comment surprised me. I thought for sure Teiso would take the side of the poor black man. I told him I didn't want to tell the owner, but he agreed with the German couple and said, "They are right, telling is the right thing to do."

Surprise. Right again. I was liking this Teiso more all the time.

He must have lain awake last night thinking of things and people to show me today. I spent most of the day seeing his world through his eyes. He was so cute the way he wanted me to meet his brother's wife, his cousin's friend, his last year's neighbor, and to see his old school. Who was I? He made me feel so included, so much a part. It was as if our two worlds weren't really any different. All of his friends made me feel so welcome. How could I have met him only yesterday, and today we were as comfortable as if we were old friends?

The more I observed the poor people, the more I was left wondering. Some of the men seemed pleasant. I couldn't detect any anger, even though they were living in such poverty. Others however seemed to resent the fact that I was an American. How dare I come and spy. Was I so curious that I just had to come and witness their meager existence for myself?

Now the word integrity began to take on a whole new meaning for me. It still meant being totally honest, giving your word and sticking to it; these concepts remain the same for everyone whether you're rich, middle class, or poor. Yet the poor have an added burden. Can a man be poor, even if it is only temporary, and fight off the feelings of envy, of comparing his situation with others and of always asking himself and those closest to him, why me? It's the "poor me" syndrome. I don't know if I could overcome this challenge. I remember being what I thought was poor. I remember hating it, but at least I had a light at the end of my tunnel, I knew it was only a matter of time and I would be normal again. Did any of these people have such a light?

Today I felt very privileged. It was indeed an honor to meet humble, poor men who had reached, in the face of poverty, a level of integrity you or I can only hope for. They gave off no feelings of "poor me." No, quite the opposite. The fact is they made me feel as if I was their equal, that they really liked me, and it was easy for me to tell that they did, and I liked them back.

How many times had I heard my children say, "That's not fair?" Well, I wish they could truly see what was "not fair."

Teiso and I had shot two rolls of film, all of them on the children. I was sure Jenny would have lots of touching pictures to choose from. But I would go home with more than pictures. Seeing those pictures will bring to my mind some fond memories, memories to last a lifetime.

I could just imagine being home for a while settling back into the routine, going to pick up my pictures, and then as soon as I saw the faces of those schoolkids all running toward me at once, each one wanting me to take their picture, some of them crying because they were sure I didn't take theirs, it would all come back to me.

I was about to take my last two pictures when Teiso said, "What about me?"

He had been so good to help, and I kept telling him that I would save the last two pictures for him.

We had a hard time finding my new lodge. There was an Africa de Ville, a Ville d'Afrique, and an African Villa, but only on our last try did he find Africa Vista. I had decided to stay at a new lodge. We did some checking around and this one was more in my price range. As we pulled into my new lodge, I asked Teiso, " If I could send you anything from the States, what would it be?"

"A radio."

I reminded him that our plugs and outlets were different than his. But he just smiled and said, "If you send it, I will make it work."

"Okay."

Then I had him stand next to his old red taxi with its broken windshield and a coat hanger for an antenna, and I shot my last two pictures. He looked so proud.

He didn't have to help me with my bags, there wasn't much left in them. I had brought extra clothing and I planned on giving it all to the people in Zambia. But, instead, I gave it to Mapenzi to give to his wife for opening her home to me. After lots of goodbyes and thank yous, Teiso was off.

A picture may capture the sight,
but to feel it, to smell it, to experience it,
you have to be there.

14

Queasy on the Zambezi

Now the next big surprise was that my new lodge was what they called self-catering. I had been living off those wonderful free breakfasts at The Zambezi Lodge. I soon found out what this self-catering meant: no soap, no shampoo, no meals. I found one small bar of free soap in my purse so it would do for my laundry, my shampoo, and my dish soap.

My room was a kitchenette made for four people. It had two bedrooms and was very nice. I felt funny having all this to myself. Once again, it was run by black men, and the owner only stayed for the day. The owner was a big man who looked almost Polynesian. He said that although they didn't cook meals if I let him know ahead of time he would be happy to get me what I needed. I told him my stomach was quite upset so if he could just get me sandwiches and yogurt I would be happy.

I wanted to call Tansy and let her know I was okay, so I asked if he had a phone. He said he did and he would stay late that night just so I could use it after my sunset cruise on the Zambezi River. Tansy would be home then.

I didn't have dinner the previous night and my stomach began to feel a bit queasy today; I hadn't eaten much of anything all day. As I was leaving the Zambezi Lodge I asked the man who was cleaning my room if he wanted these crackers and cookies I had brought in my pack. Next to them sat some old bananas that were way too old and brown for me. He asked, "And the bananas too?"

I smiled and said, "Yes, the bananas too."

He got so excited and thanked me over and over again.

By the time my ride came I was feeling even worse. I thought some yogurt and crackers would make me feel better. So when my ride came I was ready to ask if he could take me to a store. The driver turned out to be the man in the van who drove me around the first day. He didn't need to pick up anyone else so I asked him if he had time to take me to a grocery store.

"A what?"

"A place where I could get some bananas."

"Oh, yes the market."

He drove me to a pretty big store. Then I asked him if he was staying in the van. He replied, "Yes."

"Then will you watch my wallet for me?"

"Sure."

So I grabbed out a small bill and then set my purse on the seat. I didn't feel safe taking it in the store. Inside I started searching for bananas and yogurt. It didn't take long before I noticed I was the only white in the whole store. It took even less time for the people in the store to notice. I wondered if this was a store for blacks only. Up front, after you have what you came for, they had lines with those zigzagging ropes, the kind they use in amusement parks to keep the crowds in an orderly line.

I stood there waiting my turn patiently, acting like I came in there all the time. When I got up to the front, the checker asked, "Didn't you mark your bananas?"

He called for a manager. The tension began to mount. I'm sure all eyes were on me. I tried to defend myself, "I didn't know I had to mark them. I thought you would."

Now a little man acting very busy came up. He grabbed the bananas, and the checker said, "She didn't mark them."

Perceiving the whole situation, he started to laugh. "Well, then I guess they are free today."

He made everyone laugh, including me.

When I walked outside the driver was leaning on the car with his arms folded in front of him. It was almost as if he was proud to be guarding my wallet.

When we got to the river I saw I was the only one for the cruise. I asked if anyone else was coming and wondered if he would really take this big boat out with only me on board. I was relieved when he said, "Yes, the others are meeting us here."

Now the taxi driver became the boat driver.

We waited for a while, then three ladies appeared walking up the dirt road that led to the boat. They looked to be in their sixties. They were laughing and speaking in a language that I couldn't understand.

We positioned ourselves equally on the boat, two on each side. The woman sitting next to me spoke English so she asked where I was from. After explaining it to them in my usual fashion, it surprised me when the one sitting next to me said, "Oh, my friend here is going to Utah!"

"Really?"

"Yes, she has to get some testing done at the University Hospital in Salt Lake City."

So the world is becoming a smaller place. She would speak to me in English and then turn to her friends and speak to them in their native tongue, which was Dutch.

I asked her if she could speak Afrikaans since she was Dutch.

"No, not really. It has been so long since the Dutch first settled there that their language has changed over time---similar to the Americans and the British, yet far worse."

She handed me her binoculars. "Here you will need these, this is my third time on this cruise and we only come for the booze." They all had a good laugh, then she added, "They call it the sunset cruise, but we call it the booze cruise."

I had to pass on anything to drink. The man was surprised at my passing up free drinks. He said, "Drink up, you paid for it."

"I'm sorry, but I have a very sensitive stomach right now."

"Oh, the poor girl has the jungle rot, or is it the traveler's trots?"

They broke out laughing again but this time they apologized. Then each one tried giving me advice.

"When you purchase bottled water, make sure the seal has not been broken. Many of these kids selling water in the streets go around and find empty water bottles, then go to a tap and fill them up, then go back out to the streets looking for some poor soul to sell them to."

"Great," I sighed. I didn't remember if the seal was broken or not.

"Madam, try a little Coca-Cola."

"Whatever you do in this heat, don't stop drinking."

And *they* didn't---believe me!

Just then we saw a great splash come up out of the water near the opposite bank.

"There they are!" everyone shouted. They must have seen them on their other trips because they seemed to be expecting them.

It was hippos! Lots of hippos. Big ones, baby ones, two of them came up snapping at a bird both at the same time. I said to the driver, "Let's pull the boat up next to them."

"Oh, no, madam, hippos get upset very easily. They have been known to tip boats over. We must stay a safe distance away."

They were so huge, much bigger than I had imagined they would be.

I thanked the woman, over and over again for the use of her binoculars. When I looked through them, it looked as if I could touch the hippos.

That was just the beginning of a delightful cruise. We went quite a ways up the river and saw many crocodiles, which didn't seem to mind if we sailed right next to them. The river is so big that it has all kinds of islands in it; I couldn't tell the shoreline from the islands. With such a blue sky and not a cloud in sight we could see the great mist that rose up from the Falls; it looked like a cloud.

The man on the boat told me his version of the Dr. Livingstone legend.

"This was the way Dr. Livingstone first saw the Falls. He rode on a canoe with the natives exactly where our little boat is heading."

I liked to lay back and imagine I was him, seeing all of this for the first time: the giant palm trees, the crocodiles, the hippos, the zebras, and, of course, the Falls.

He continued, "We believe that he liked it so much, when they tried to get him to go back, he refused. And the story goes that he stayed here until he died of malaria. The natives always treated him well; they were the ones who took care of him until he died."

We saw some boys fishing on the Zambian side of the river. We teased with them to show us their fish. They said, "Come over here and we will sell them to you." We laughed.

The boat driver said this was as close as we could get to the Zambian side without getting a fine.

After we returned to shore and said our goodbyes, my driver seemed to be in a big hurry. He started driving really fast on the dirt roads; it was making me nervous. Suddenly I saw something big in the bush so I cried out, "Stop!"

"What is it?"

"I don't know. Something in there, in the bush, I thought I saw something move."

He looked, I looked, and then as we sat there quietly a massive water buffalo stepped out to eat the grass along the side of the road.

"That's what you stopped me for?!"

Well, I thought it was cool. Obviously he didn't.

When I got back to the lodge I ran in to call Tansy. Tembeka answered. When I heard her voice it felt as if I were speaking to my own family. Then when Tansy got on the phone, even though it had only been a week, it seemed much longer than that. A funny feeling came over me; it was as if civilization was far away. I started to tell her everything I had seen all at once. She interrupted and calmly said, "Peggy, this call is very expensive; tell me when you get home, okay?"

She was right. I ended our call by saying, "See you in a few days. Please make sure someone is there to pick me up. Thank you. Tell the family hello. 'Bye."

Just like that I was on my own again.

That night I was miserable. I had the jungle gomboo and the same uneasy feelings with the night watchmen walking by my room.

In the morning I walked down to the room where the only other people staying at the Lodge were. They were out late last night. I'm not sure what time they got in. I knew that they weren't there when I went to bed, or I would have talked with them last night.

Not wanting to wait a moment longer, I went over to ask if they had anything I could take or if they had any advice on what to do for my gomboo. I had spent a long sleepless night last night, and wasn't in the mood to repeat it. They were very helpful. They gave me some Immodium and told me to eat only toast and black coffee for breakfast. Then they said to take two now and one tonight and it should take care of it. I thanked them cordially and was invited to have breakfast with them.

At breakfast we discussed the possibility of driving into Zambia. I told them I was all for it, depending on how I felt in an hour or so. They assured me I would feel better within the hour. It had worked for one of them.

This might be the first time I have said this and I think it's high time I did: too many good things were falling into place for me. I stopped believing in coincidence a long time ago. Someone had to be watching out for me, someone who knew me better than I knew myself. I had got myself in some pretty tight situations, and I had the tendency to get into even worse.

I wanted to go to Zambia so badly I was ready to go by myself if I had to. I had even said to myself, if I feel better by tomorrow, I will go. I had not come all this way just to stop now. Well, what do you know, here it was today, and in two hours I was on my way to Zambia! Coincidence?

Sometimes we look too far,
when what we are looking for
is right in front of us.

15

Zambia

Families, no two are ever exactly alike. But the personalities of the people in them can be so similar. My new friends turned out to be two sisters, Kim and Sandy, and their two friends, Jerry and Joy. The older sister Kim lived in Cape Town. The younger one, Sandy, lived in England. These two sisters reminded me so much of my own sister and me. They had rented a car for the week and had thought about going to Zambia several times but hadn't been there yet.

We weren't sure if you could drive over the border, but with what Nkosi had told me about the Falls on the Zambian side, we wanted to try. When we got to the border these two really began to shine. The older sister said, staring at all the poor black people in line, "I don't think we should drive our car across the border."

The younger one said, "Oh, come on, we planned on going over."

"I don't know, it just doesn't appear to be a good idea."

I was thinking to myself, come on, don't give up yet. The younger one said, "What do you mean, 'doesn't appear to be a good idea'?"

"I mean I don't think our car will be safe. This is a rental car and we are responsible for it."

"Okay, fine. You stay here with the car and we are going to walk across."

"I can't just wait with the car. Who knows how long you'll be?"

Great! Right about now I started thinking I should leave these two and go grab a taxi by myself. I had already got a visa way back in October, which gave me permission to enter Zambia. Here it was February, and I was bound and determined to use it.

Now these two were really going at it.

"I have done everything you wanted me to do on this whole trip! All I want to do is go into Zambia to see the Falls from that side and perhaps see the trinkets the people make over there."

"Look. Maybe we should just walk across the bridge. That would give us some time to think about it once we get over." (The border post was on the other side of the bridge.)

"Then, if you don't want to go, you can stay and watch the bungee- jumpers, okay?"

To this we all agreed; we would leave the car on the Zimbabwe side and walk across the bridge.

While we were crossing the bridge we all stopped to watch the world's highest bungee fall. It took our stomachs away just to look over the side of the bridge, let alone jump. It was so far down that there was no way for one rope to pull you back up. After you jump they send a second guy down on a rope half as long as the first, he pulls you up halfway, then the man from on top pulls you the rest of the way up.

I overheard a man standing next to me telling some friends about the bridge. He said that when they were building it they calculated precisely each metal piece they would need. Then a company in England contracted to build the pieces. They began construction of the bridge starting with the sides first. As each piece was flown in they noticed that in the heat of the day the metal would swell, so when they were on their very last piece they had to lower it into place in the early morning before the day got hot, and it fitted perfectly.

Once we were in about the middle of the bridge we could look way down the gorge. Kim pointed out to us the very first hotel built at Victoria Falls. The vegetation was so thick we could barely see it, but there sticking out of the trees, we caught a glimpse of it. This beautiful building was built by the British in 1904. It was called the Victoria Falls Hotel. To stay there cost about two hundred U.S. dollars per night.

Once over the bridge, we were in Zambia. The sisters went into the border post; one bought a visa and the other said she didn't have any zims and that's all they would take. Whether that was true or not I ended up going into Zambia with the younger sister and her friend. I was disappointed that Kim and Jerry were not coming along. Joy was the neutral party of the group who thought it was her duty to explain both sisters to me. She had no way of knowing everything these two argued about!---made perfect sense to me.

Zambia! I could finally say I had visited Tansy's homeland if only for a day. I wished I could have seen more, but the images, the beauty, the poverty I saw there I shall not forget. Someday I hope to return and visit Tansy with all her family together again.

When we arrived back at our lodge, the sisters were back to being best of friends. They all went out for the evening.

I stayed behind to have a quiet dinner here at the Lodge. I had some crackers (they were called Digestive Biscuits. Is that supposed to sound appetizing, or what?) and some bananas, none of which sounded very good. I went to ask the men if they were going to cook up something for supper tonight.

As I walked into the little office, the employees seemed so somber. They said, "No supper tonight."

They weren't in an arguing mood I could tell.

I walked over to look in the fridge hoping to find something good to eat. The first thing I noticed was tons of yogurt. I had forgotten that I had asked for it; obviously the owner hadn't.

"Where is the owner?" I asked.

"He's got malaria, madam. He's too sick to come in."

So that explained the long faces. I knew how much they depended on this job; if anything should happen to him they would all lose their jobs.

This was the third person I had met with malaria. I began trying to remember if I had put on mosquito repellent that day. It made me wonder if the same mosquito that had bitten him was still hanging around. Then I looked back at this nice man who seemed sad but calm and I asked, "This may sound like a dumb question, but aren't you afraid of getting malaria, or do you somehow become immune to it?"

"Immune?"

"I mean, have you been around it so long you can't get it anymore?"

"Oh no, madam. Every day people I know get it and even die from it. That is just the way it is. It will do no good to worry about it."

I didn't even know the owner but I felt bad for him and these nice people. I got a can of pop out of the refrigerator and asked if he would be back tomorrow. They didn't know.

When I turned to head back to my room, I couldn't help noticing a bulletin board hanging on the wall just outside the office. It was full of places to go and things to see while you were in Zimbabwe, some local news, and a few quotations. Something caught my eye; it was a poem. As I sat there reading it I liked it so much I knew I had to get a copy. I ran back to my room, grabbed a piece of paper and a pen, and started writing.

Attitude   by Charles Swindal

The longer I live, the more I realize the impact of attitude on my life.
Attitude, to me is more important than facts.
It is more important than the past, than education, than money, than circumstances, than failures, than successes, than what other people think or say or do.
It is more important than appearance, giftedness, or skill.
It will make or break a company, a church, a home.
The remarkable thing is we have a choice everyday regarding the attitude we will embrace for that day.
We cannot change the past. We cannot change the fact that people will act in a certain way.
We cannot change the inevitable.
The only thing we can do is play on the one string we have, and that is our attitude.
I am convinced that life is ten percent what happens to me and ninety percent how I react to it.
And so it is with you, we are in charge of our attitudes.

This little poem made me think that all of the people I had met so far must carry a copy of it with them. I had never seen such optimism. With the exception of Mugunda, the frustrated future student, I hadn't met anyone with the negative attitudes that I am always faced with back home. People giving you the feeling like I don't have to be nice to you, this is just my job. I used to wonder if it would take the girls at the grocery store, the men at the drivers license bureau, especially the ones in the big cities, any more effort to smile and be pleasant than to frown and say, "Next!"

For me, this little poem summed up the country side of Africa.

I ran back to my room, closed all the windows and doors, poured on mosquito repellent and hoped to be able to make it home to show this to my family and friends.

Alone in my room, sitting here pondering for hours, thinking and reminiscing, I was glad for this quiet time when I was able to put my life on rewind. I was glad I thought back on my childhood, glad I thought back on a time when I thought I was poor and glad I had remembered my unique friend Tansy. She was the whole reason I had this time, why I had so much to think about, and why my life will be better for having known her. I was thinking of my day spent with Sandy and Joy, wondering why on this whole trip I had met up with nothing but kind people, thinking about Teiso, Isaac, and Mapenzi.

How is this kindness possible when human nature is supposed to be so carnal, so evil, especially in this day and age? I wanted to shout and tell the world, "Stop showing me all the evil! Start restoring my faith in mankind and start showing me the good in people."

I think the media is much at fault for this, but is it true that we the American people would rather see an awful, terrifying story than a good one? I have learned one thing: under any circumstances, kindness is possible!

All evening I had been alone and still tonight I would be alone. But I had enjoyed being alone. It was the only way I could take a good look at my life, look at my mistakes, see what I had learned, be determined to change what I could, and rid myself of bitterness at the things I could not. Being alone is different than being lonely. Yes, I was afraid---afraid of all the dangers that being alone could bring---but here in the middle of Africa, I was not lonely.

I was no longer just an American, but I had the feeling I was now part of something bigger: the family of man.

*There will be times in your life when
you must put yourself into someone else's hands,
and hope that they will deliver you.*

16

Sunday Morning

It was a beautiful Sunday morning. What made it so much more beautiful was the fact that I was going home today. I had seen what I had come for and hopefully I had learned the lessons I was supposed to learn. I was actually looking forward to the three-day bus ride. I gathered up what used to be my belongings but were now transformed into woodcarvings. Wondering what I would do until the bus arrived, I went over to ask if the TV in my front room worked. I hadn't taken the time to ask about it before.

I found one of the night watchmen leaning against a post next to the office. He was listening to what looked like an old transistor radio. I could barely hear it but I could tell it was African music in a language that I couldn't begin to understand. Almost every black person I had met spoke such good English that it almost made me forget that he had his own language. He was humming along.

I said, "Excuse me."

He turned around quickly; I had startled him.

"I'm sorry, I didn't mean to scare you."

"Not a problem, madam. How can I help you?"

"Well, I wondered if that TV in my room worked."

"Oh, you want to watch TV?"

"Yes, if I could."

"Okay. I will turn the satellite on. Please come and tell me if it doesn't work for you. Okay?"

"Okay. Thank you." I went back to my room.

This lodge was so different than the last. The last one, owned by a woman, was so rustic-looking inside. It had all kinds of hunting equipment and stuffed animals everywhere. This one, owned by a man, was so frilly inside: flowered curtains, bedspreads, and all with matching décor. It even had all of the modern conveniences: a stove, a swamp cooler, a kitchen sink; it even had a TV.

So here I sat waiting to see if the TV worked. I was not a big TV watcher but when I have time I enjoy a good, stimulating TV show. Now I certainly had time.

Looking out my window, waiting for my TV to be turned on, the irony of this whole situation came clear to me. The two night watchmen would walk back and forth from the tiny office to these two tiny huts that sit right in front of a big wooden gate. Their entire job consists of protecting the guests from the outside world. Sitting in their chairs all night wasn't what I would consider a stressful job. None of the jobs were stressful. Whether you were in charge of cleaning of rooms, or doing laundry, there just wasn't much stress involved. I wondered if this lack of stress contributed to the pleasant nature everyone seemed to have.

Just as I was thinking how peaceful and content these people seemed to be, what came on TV---Oprah! And what was the topic of her show: Eliminating Stress from Your Life.

She had many guests who had simply had it. They were stressed to their limit. A doctor came on and tried to help these people decide what was important, and to eliminate what wasn't. Contentions arose in the audience as people struggled to come to an agreement on what was important and what was not.

With the frame of mind I was in right now I felt as if none of it was worth the stress. Getting kids to practices, going all out to entertain guests, decorating our homes just right for the holidays, being expected to turn out and support every family, work, and friends' special event, and if you don't show up, dealing with the guilt put on you because you didn't, trying to reach your full potential at no matter what the cost. Stop! Ask yourself, is it all worth it? NO!

So how do we get back to simply enjoying life? I had seen so many happy people with almost no material possessions living a quiet, simple life and enjoying it. What were we doing wrong?

After being handed so much to think about, I turned off the TV. Was someone trying to tell me something, or what?

The absolute silence sounded good. Outside, all the green surrounding the still, blue pool looked so soothing. I walked outside and sat down on a chair under a large tree, my bags resting next to me.

After a few moments the night watchman came over and sat down by me.

"Did the TV work for you, madam?"

"Yes. Thank you."

"You are going home today, madam?"

"Yes, my bus leaves in a few hours."

"You have enjoyed Vic Falls, I hope?"

"Yes, it was all so beautiful."

"Do you have any waterfalls by you?"

"Not like these." I could tell he wanted to visit so I reached into my things and took out my silk pouch of pictures.

"These are some pictures of where I am from. These are my flower gardens. I love flowers. This is my home. This is a mountain which we climb every summer."

I showed him two pictures of Mt. Timpanogos. One had my family and some friends in the middle of a meadow filled with wild flowers. The other was the glacier that never melts.

"When you get really hot and tired of climbing your reward is to slide down the glacier."

He had many questions; these are things he had never seen before: pine trees, snow, rocky mountain tops, meadows--- how could I even begin to explain? I decided to tell him by using things in nature that I knew he was familiar with.

"Back home we have mosquitoes too. But they do not give us malaria, they are just a bother because they sting and then you itch. Do you have dragonflies?"

"Yes, madam. Red dragonflies."

"We have dragonflies too. In fact at home one of my favorite sights is what we call the dragonfly migration. Our house sits right at the foot of a big mountain. The mountain is our backyard. In front of our house it is very flat. When it rains, it forms big puddles. The puddles get so big and the land is so flat that the water can't go anywhere. It sits there and becomes a marsh. Only plants that can live in standing water grow there: tall, thick bladed grass and cattails."

I had to explain cattails. Yes, he had some of those too. I continued: "The dragonflies for some reason like to fly up in the mountains at night and fly down to the wetlands in the day. Every morning just as the sun comes up over the mountain, it begins to warm the world below. You can go outside and see thousands of dragonflies flying just over your head; they are all around you. They make no noise; they just seem to be gliding on air. The sunlight touches each wing, making them shimmer just like sparkling glass. Now the air all around you is alive and moving with hundreds of tiny sparkles. They pay no attention to you; they are on their way down to the marsh below and nothing can stop them.

"Every evening the same thing happens right at dusk. They all start their flight up the mountain. This time the air sparkles more orange and red. They fly up silhouetted against a beautiful sunset, making it appear as tiny golden windows. It's a quiet affair. If you weren't right there when it happens, you would never experience this beautiful sight.

"Once my husband, who knows I love to watch the dragonflies, said to me, 'Peggy, what if you could get rid of the mosquitoes but you had to give up the dragonflies, would you do it?'

"Ooh, he knows I hate the mosquitoes. I answered without hesitation, 'No way!'"

The young night watchman didn't seem too busy to listen, didn't seem bothered that I took up his time; he just sat there and enjoyed each word.

We heard a little whistle and both looked up at the same time to see the owner coming. I had been worried about him and was happy to see him.

He looked pale and beads of sweat were pouring off his forehead. I could tell he didn't feel at all well.

"Well, hello. Are you feeling any better?"

"Not much. I went down to get a shot this morning. I'm hoping that will help."

"I didn't know if you were going to come in today."

"I wasn't until I remembered you had to check out today. What time does your bus come?"

"About noon. I'm sorry, I made you come in today."

Just then I remembered all the yogurt in the fridge. "Thanks so much for the yogurt."

"You're welcome."

He was very weak. I really did wish he had stayed in bed today. He assured me he would only take the time to get me checked out then go straight back to bed.

I only had fifty rands left so I asked if he took Visa. I wasn't sure what kind of hassles I would have at the borders on the way home so I wanted to save my cash.

"Yes, Visa would be fine." He knew us civilized people all too well. Buy now pay later. All over the world people are catching on to this. I guess that truly means the world is becoming smaller.

I thanked him and told him I loved his poem.

"Which poem?"

"Attitude."

"Oh yes, that is a good one."

Still I could tell he wasn't in too talkative a mood. He thanked me politely, shoved all the papers into his drawer, closed up his office, and went home. I knew malaria could kill you. I also knew the doctors were doing what they could. At this point his fate was out of his hands. I was touched that this man who did not know me was there to help, even with this life-threatening condition.

The safari-looking man (the one with the sign) who drove me to my first lodge showed up to take me back to the post office. I was really glad to see him. I had these nightmares all night that I had missed the bus and had to stay another week. Don't get me wrong. It wasn't the place; it was my situation and the money. I couldn't have been stuck in a more beautiful, more friendly place. I just wish I'd had someone to share it with.

Fear is relative,
it is directly related to your knowledge,
more specifically, your lack of knowledge.

17

Return to Table Mountain

Sometimes I find it funny the things I worry about only to find out later there wasn't anything to worry about. Before I left Cape Town I imagined Victoria Falls to be the same as Niagara Falls. I wondered if I would be able to find a taxi once I got to the post office. Now the post office ended up being the only drop-off in Victoria Falls, and all of the taxis waited there. That must be why Tansy's friend at the Embassy looked at me so strangely when I insisted I had better pay for a taxi ahead of time, just to be sure.

Now I kept nervously turning my ticket over and over again, checking to make sure I knew what time the bus was going to pick me up and wondering if it would even show. My young safari-looking man could tell I was nervous so he said, "Would you like me to stay with you until the bus arrives?" I sure did.

Talking with him got my mind off other things, things that were out of my hands anyway. He said he had always wanted to go to America.

"You should come," I said, "you can stay at my house. I would show you the mountains with the snow on top that never melts. I would show you the red rock country where the wind has carved holes through solid rock to form arches. It wouldn't cost you anything once you got there."

"Oh, I would love to see it all. But you see, madam, I could never afford to go to America."

"Yes you could, just save your money like I did."

"No, you do not understand. I would have to save up thirty-eight times what you did to go there."

That concept really hit home to me. I had not even thought of this before. None of my friends will ever be able to come visit me in Utah. None of these people could ever leave here, no matter how badly they wanted to. They were having a hard enough time just living day to day but to save for a trip that would cost thirty-eight times what I saved would be unthinkable. Then I realized for the first time how truly unique my meeting Tansy and being her friend was. It had to be more than a coincidence. When she and Nkosi move back to Zambia it will cost them four hundred times what it will cost me. Oh, the faith of a child. Just before I left, Tembeka said to me, "I am going to start saving all my money so I can come and stay with you, Auntee."

At last my bus showed up and I was in my seat. I felt a huge rush of relief hit me.

As funny as it may seem I was actually looking forward to these two nights on the bus. I guess safety is relative. Some people wouldn't feel safe on a bus, but after being by myself night after night in the middle of some foreign country where their culture is so different than mine I actually felt safe on the bus.

As we were pulling out of Vic Falls, I wanted to somehow hold on to everything I could see outside. I knew I might never be back.

Experience is the best teacher, right? By now I knew just what to expect on the bus, so I was prepared. I had brought a bag full of tissue paper. The little holes the bus stopped at never had toilet paper. I even brought enough to share. I knew that even though I liked to visit, I would get a much better night's sleep if I tried to take up two seats. This wouldn't be hard since only seven people got on the bus.

I hate to admit it but I was in no mood to meet anyone. I was on my way home. I just stared out the window feeling more like being entertained than entertaining.

Twice we passed a family of monkeys sitting on the side of the road, all lined up in single file. As we passed by, their faces all turned simultaneously to watch the bus go by. I suppose even they were awed by this big newcomer that stirred up all the dust as it passed.

We passed a sign that read, "Watch for elephants crossing." Believe me, I was. I would stare out the window into the jungle and let my imagination run wild. It was kind of fun being in my own little world.

All too soon reality hit. We were at our first border post; get ready for the hassle. Here at Botswana the two border officials decided to get on the bus, I guess just to check us out. They said hello to each person one by one and stood there looking at us and our bags until we all squirmed a bit. They did this to everyone on the bus. Big deal, eight people. I don't know what they wanted but they made us wait one whole hour. Then they just said, "OKAY!"

At one little town we stopped to gas up. It took another hour, I'm not sure why. So while we were waiting I started watching a group of people across the street. It looked like just a place to hang out. It was mostly teenagers. I kept watching this old red car pull up. Everyone was laughing and seemed to be having a good time. Many people would all get into the car, then loaded down, half of the people hanging out the windows, it would speed off. Typical teenagers I thought. Then later it would come back still filled with people they would get out and more people would pile in.

On the third go round I figured it out. This was the meeting place if you wanted to catch a taxi or a car bus as I called them. The last time there were at least ten people standing around with all their bags and stuff. I thought to myself, there's no way he'll fit all of that into his car.

It was better than any comedy I had ever seen. People started sitting on each other's laps, he roped some luggage up on top, opened the trunk, and crammed more luggage in it. Last of all this big fat man walked around and around the car studying the situation. I thought, no way! But he just opened the back door, sat on the edge, and pushed himself halfway in. Then he stuck his enormous arm out the window and held the door half shut. The driver walked around giving it a once-over, then gave his tires a kick. Seeing that everything was okay he got in and away they went. Cruising down the dirt road it looked like it was riding on a cloud of dust.

Now as the bus drove along into the evening, I could see lots of little fires glowing in the center of the little villages. It must be suppertime. I could see mothers trying to shoo their little ones away from the fire and tired fathers sitting down with their backs leaning up against the huts. I could almost picture everyone asking mum, "When will it be ready?"

I had noticed that when I went shopping with Tansy's children they never once asked, "Can we buy this?" or "Let's get this!" I'm sure these little ones couldn't be too demanding either. What good would it do to ask for more when they know there isn't any more?

The air was so still and so damp that each fire made a perfectly straight line of smoke. As I looked over the landscape, the greens began to turn to shades of pink, the lines of smoke looked even straighter with the backdrops of silhouetted, jagged trees. It was all so peaceful.

It was six a.m. when we got to Windhoek, Namibia. I was not looking forward to spending twelve hours here again.

When you don't know anyone, a familiar face is a welcome sight. At the bus station, working behind the desk, was the same girl who had watched my bags a week ago. I joked with her and said, "You'll have to put up with me for another day."

To that she replied sleepily, "I can put up with anything. I just spent all day yesterday and all last night in this stupid bus station. I am waiting for someone to come and spell me, but he is late as usual."

I gave her ten rands to watch my bags and this time I trusted her. I walked all over the city. When I got back to the bus station, there was the same boy who had charged me for the phone call last week.

I sat there with nothing to do, waiting, waiting, waiting. A man came up to me and said, "Are you an American?"

"Yes, how did you know?"

"From your accent."

He pulled up a chair and sat right next to me. "I have been looking for an American for three years. Madam, this is urgent. Please listen carefully."

I was a little surprised with the urgency but I thought, sure, why not? I haven't got anything else to do.

He continued "Now, madam. I am from Liberia, do you know where Liberia is?"

"No." I hadn't even heard of Liberia.

"Madam, it is so important for me to find an American. Are you listening to me?" He must have asked me if I was listening to him fifty times.

"Yes, yes."

"Okay. Do you know why we trust Americans in my country?"

"No."

"Liberia, madam, is where Americans came to get their slaves then when the slaves were returned, they returned them to Liberia, thus the capital Monrovia, named after President Monroe. So, madam, we were settled by Americans. My country has been in a civil war for the last six years. On my father's land we had some German people cutting down the trees. Not long ago we noticed they were not replanting the trees as they were supposed to. Are you listening to me?"

"Yes"

"Now the Germans found gold on my father's land. They did not want us to know so they were just taking it in their pockets. When my father found out, we drove them off our land. Now my family is digging the gold with---" he mimicked digging.

I said, "Shovels, picks?"

"Yes, madam, and the war is now over and we are desperate; no one has got paid. My family sent me here to Namibia to find someone to help. I need to go back; I promised my father. He grows concerned. He is old now; he is counting on me. We need machines; we need help. Please, madam, do you see we need your help?"

"Yes, but . . ."

"Madam, all you have to do is go back home and tell someone. If they will just come, I will show them. Then they will believe."

"I don't know if I can help; no one will believe me." I didn't know if I believed him.

180

"All I am asking is, send someone to come look."

"I don't know if anyone will believe me." I couldn't quite get him to understand.

He said, "Okay, I will go get my cousin. He will tell you, then you will know it is the truth. What time does your bus leave?"

I said, "Six o'clock."

"I'll be back in one hour with my cousin."

Surprisingly, my in-laws were in the mining assay business. I knew a few things about mining. I certainly knew what placer gold was and I knew it was interesting to hear about.

The boy behind the desk who had been watching my bags for me asked why that man was talking to me for so long. "It looked so important, so pressing."

I shrugged my shoulders then playfully answered, "Oh, it was nothing important. He just owns a gold mine in Liberia, that's all."

He started laughing. "Sure he does. He came in to use the phone and couldn't afford to pay his bill. Now he's telling you he has a gold mine." He started to laugh again.

He started joking with me, so I joked right back with him.

"Hey, if I get rich I'll send you some, besides he is sending his cousin here to tell me it's the truth. Laugh now, but when his cousin comes, then you will believe." Another good joke for both of us.

It was about an hour and here came Lweendo with another man who he introduced as his cousin James. Then he turned to James, "Do I have a gold mine?"

"Yes!"

"There you go, proof that what I am saying is true."

I told him I did not know what I could do but I would ask when I got home and see if there was anyone who would come and look. He was thankful. I told him that all I could do was try. Yes, I would try. He gave me an address where I could reach him in Liberia, and I gave him mine. The boy behind the desk, who stood watching, just smiled at me and I smiled back. Another day at the bus station.

After waiting forever, I saw my bus pull up, at least I thought it was my bus. A black lady dressed all in exquisite clothing and jewelry came running up, "Is this the bus to Cape Town?"

"Yes," someone answered. She motioned to another black lady, "Hurry up with those bags."

I really couldn't believe what I was seeing. It looked as if the poorly dressed black lady was waiting on the fancily dressed black lady. A black servant waiting on a black woman. Oh, well, whatever. At least I now knew this was my bus.

Many people got on this time, but no whites. As I handed my ticket to the attendant she said, "This ticket is dated for yesterday."

I had no idea what the date was today; I had kind of lost track of time. She insisted that this ticket was supposed to be used yesterday.

"Look," I said, "I couldn't have used this yesterday, I was on a bus leaving Victoria Falls yesterday."

She took my ticket to the driver and I grew more concerned. People were growing a little restless because they wanted to get on the bus. She came back and said, "Take a seat upstairs."

I replied, "Thank you."

I got a window seat and set my bags on the seat next to me.

At about three a.m. we came to the South African border. I had no problem crossing, but I'm sorry I can't say that about everyone on the bus. Some of the black men didn't have the papers they needed to cross, so they were not allowed back on the bus. It reminded me of similar times on the Mexican border when people try to cross into the States.

When the sun came up I saw farmlands. I knew where I was now for the first time on my whole trip. Many times I would say to myself, you could be on the wrong bus and you would never know it. I had no maps and I didn't know any of the town names.

By noon the next day I could see Table Mountain in the distance. I started to get so excited inside. I was never that impressed with Table Mountain, but it looked so good to me right now. It proved like nothing else could that I was on the right bus. I was almost home.

Sharing how you feel
with someone you really care about
may seem unimportant at the time,
but sometimes, . . . to that person,
it makes all the difference in the world!

18
Expressions of Love

When the bus pulled into Cape Town I looked out the window at the little crowd of people waiting for the bus. I couldn't see Nkosi or Tansy so I took my time getting off. I was the last one off the bus.

Now I could see Nkosi. His worried face turned to a huge grin when he saw me. I ran up to him and he gave me a big hug. To see his familiar face tickled me inside, and I think he felt the same way.

As we walked to his car I was talking his head off as usual, only this time Nkosi was excited and actually interested.

"How was your ride? How was the weather? What did you think of the Falls? Who did you meet? Tell me everything, Peggy."

I just went on and on. He was so happy for me. We had such a good time talking about the places he loves, and now I loved them too. I would talk about how beautiful Zambia was, he would just smile. I would talk about the bridge between Zimbabwe and Zambia, he would just smile. I would talk about the beautiful woodcarvings, the hippos, the crocodiles, and the corn gardens scattered in the trees, he would just smile. I knew he missed his home.

It wasn't until I said, "I never realized how far I would be traveling," that he said, "It's good to have you back."

I had not known Nkosi very well before this trip. When he was in the States he was always either in school or studying. Since I had been in Cape Town, he and I had spent many hours together, riding to see sights, waiting for Tansy to get off work, waiting to pick the kids up from school. Circumstance had forced us to get to know each other very well. I had seen him under pressure, I had seen him happy, and I had seen him sad. Always he had been a man of integrity, analyzing each situation and handling it with kindness and patience. This was a wonderful man, and I liked him very much.

Interrupting my thoughts, he spoke, "Scott has been so worried. He called this morning and said as soon as you get back to call him."

I didn't want Scott to have to worry. That's why I told him I was going with a tour. If he had any idea what I really did then I could see him worrying. I couldn't wait to talk to him. I missed my Scotty s-o-o-o-o-o much!

When we went to get in the car, Nkosi handed the man who had been watching our car a few coins. We started to drive off when someone motioned to us, "You have a flat tire."

Great. I wanted to get back because I was tired, dirty, and hungry. The only thing I had eaten all day was my last banana and some impala jerky I bought from a man in Namibia. I had never tasted such good jerky.

At least with Nkosi fixing the tire I had more time to talk. I told him about the thief who took a few dollars from my wallet and nothing else, not even the rest of my money! He said, "Sounds like a child who steals from the cookie jar. If he takes just one he figures it will never be missed."

My trip was relived over and over again as I told Nkosi all about it.

When I got home I had almost forgotten about the ritual of unlocking the many locks on the door just to go inside. There were men working in the street right next to their home. They stopped their work and stood there staring as we went into the house together. I had forgotten about that too.

After saying, "You help yourself to anything in the house, you must be very hungry and tired," he left to pick up the kids.

When I first arrived in Cape Town I was so careful not to drink the water, not to eat certain foods, and I was constantly washing my hands. Tansy would just smile. After what I had seen and lived through in the past few days I knew Cape Town wasn't about to hurt me. I felt indestructible now. I opened their fridge; everything looked so inviting. Just seeing things in a refrigerator made everything look safe to eat. I didn't worry about their water; I drank all I wanted. After all, it came from a tap. Then when I opened the cupboard I almost started to cry. There sat all the Cape Town food that I loved. The caramel cake, the cookies---called of course biscuits---their version of cold cereal, whole wheat bread. Then I looked around on the counter. In big bowls sat oranges, bananas---lots of bananas---, nectarines, and when I saw the avocados, I just about lost it. No one in their family cared for avocados, but I remember going on and on about how much I loved them and how expensive they were. Here they just grew on trees everywhere.

My dear friends, I knew they couldn't afford all this. I also knew they would never let me pay them back. I went to the phone to call Scott. He was relieved that I had made it back to Tansy's. I told him how much I loved him and missed him, and that I would tell him all about it in just a few days.

When the kids got home they were so glad to see me. When Tansy got home she gave me a giant hug, then she cooked me her wonderful chicken and soapy rice. It tasted so wonderful. I told them it would be a while before I wanted to eat another banana, and they got a good laugh out of that.

After supper Nkosi went and got his cakes. Tansy teasingly said,

"Nkosi what is this? What has happened? Do you think we are rich? Ever since Peggy has come we have more cakes than I can ever remember seeing, and they are all caramel cakes. Did you forget I like the chocolate ones?"

She winked at Nkosi. He was always trying to please.

The next day I had some business to take care of. I took Nkosi to school so I could have the car. There were pictures I wanted to take, but we kept saying there would be time later. Well later was here. I wanted to take some pictures of Nkosi's university, Tansy's university, the neighbors, flowers, and so on.

Tansy told me about a funny thing that happened while I was gone. The neighbors, who rarely even talk to them because they are the only blacks in the neighborhood, cautiously approached Tansy one day as she arrived home from work. They said they didn't know how to tell her but they thought it was their duty to let her know that her husband kept bringing home a white woman, and sometimes she would even drive their car. She started to laugh and explained to them that the white woman was her friend visiting from the States. Apologetically they said, "Oh, we'd love to meet her."

When I went to take pictures at Nkosi's university I ended up staying quite a while in the library. I found a thick book, actually many thick books, all entitled *Prominent Men in South Africa*. The first volume started at about 1750 to 1800, the next about 1800 to 1850, and from 1850 to 1900, and so on. I was not surprised when I thumbed through the pages and saw that there were no black men in any of the books. Hopefully, when the new volumes come out, that will change.

I thought about the time when Nkosi and I were sitting in the car waiting for the kids to get out of school. We were talking about this very thing and he said times were beginning to change. If I had come just four years ago, we both couldn't sit in the front seat of his car. I would drive and he would have to sit in the back. It simply wouldn't have been allowed. I felt as if I were living back in the fifties or something.

I started to notice that every time Nkosi and I spoke that he has thought things through. That must be his doctorate degree in psychology coming out. Although he rarely speaks if he is in a crowd, when you talk to him one to one you can tell that he is a very educated man. But he is always down-to- earth, modest, never thinking he is better than anyone else.

It was an unusually hot day. Our plan was that I would pick Simba and Tembeka up from school, then go to Nkosi's school to pick him up, and we would all head to the botanical gardens to pick up some seeds. I was going to try and grow some South African flowers in Utah.

After school, Nkosi asked what time my plane was leaving tomorrow. I said, "Ten o'clock at night. Why?"

"Oh, I have a department party I have to go to, but I should be back by eight. I can't miss seeing you off." He gave me a little smile.

I did not want Nkosi to know this, but I found it hard to believe he was the head of his department. It wasn't that he wasn't smart enough, it's more that he seemed too shy. Simba and Tembeka were being so good as I did my last minute running here and there stuff. Nkosi turned around and announced, "You kids have been so good, let's go for ice cream."

This had become almost an everyday thing when Nkosi, I, and the kids were in the car. McDonalds was having ninety-five cent ice-cream cones. This meant they were about fifteen cents for me. The day we first started this routine it was a very hot day. As we pulled into the drive-up to get our ninety-five cent cones, I said, "And I'll have an ice water."

Nkosi looked at me kind of worried because he always paid. I reassured him, "It's okay, they always give you ice water for free."

When he went to pay, they didn't charge him for the ice water. He thought that was so cool. From then on whenever we stopped for ice cream he would say in a most proper voice, "We'll have four ice cream cones and four ice-cold waters." I just smiled.

Tansy was tired of the braids in her hair so later that night I offered to help her take them out. I learned about native black people's hair that night, and she learned about mine. We came to the conclusion that perfect hair would be somewhere in between hers and mine. It took us about three hours to take out her braids.

I thought Tansy had grown her hair out since the last time I saw her. She told me native black people's hair will only grow so long then it either breaks off or just doesn't grow anymore. Tansy's hair is pretty short, only about five inches.

When she went home her sisters braided fake hair in with hers. They were such tiny braids that it took them about three days of steady braiding but she said it was worth it because it would stay looking good for months. It was the easiest hairstyle anyone ever had and it looked great too. I liked the way her hair felt. It was so fuzzy, soft, and fluffy.

It was good for us to spend this time together, but Tansy was being kind of quiet tonight; we both knew why. I didn't want things to get sad yet, so I tried to think of something to talk about that would make her get on a roll.

"I met a boy up in Zimbabwe that wants so bad to go to a university but can't afford it. I told him I would try to help him."

"That's the problem with you, Peggy. You want to help everyone. I don't like to discourage you, but there is no university in Vic Falls. In fact, there is only one in all of Zimbabwe and it's hundreds of kilometers away."

"Tansy, what else could I do? You know as well as I do that you are where you are because of education."

"Peggy, there are thousands of children just like him."

"What can you, one person, do? Life just isn't fair, and it is harder on some than on others."

"But if we could educate those people who are having the hard life, I believe it can only get better for them."

"Peggy, the problem is most poor children can't see this. They lack the vision. All they see is that their parents, and their parents' parents, all dropped out of school. So when they reach a certain age, and school is no longer fun, they too drop out. What will school get them? they ask."

I knew she was right, but I was determined now more than ever to try and help find a solution. There just has to be one.

This topic was too much for our last night together; I would give it more thought later. When I was on the bus I realized Tansy never talked much about her father. So I asked her, "Tell me about your father."

"Well, there isn't much to tell. He died about ten years ago. He was a quiet, shy man who adored my mom. They had known each other since they were children. They grew up in the same village. Everything she said, he would back her up. He was the lamb of the family. You could always go to him for hugs, but mom thought he was too soft with us children. I can still hear her yelling, 'Tawanda, are you gonna let Tansy get away with that?!'

"They slept on a mat together in the corner of our house. After he died we all wanted to give her a bed where we thought she would be more comfortable in her old age, but she refused. She slept on that mat in the corner till she died."

With that, Tansy thought of her mother. We were both silent. I just kept working with her hair.

We communicated much while speaking very little that evening.

The children had come in from swimming now and wanted to get in on the action. Tembeka was good at taking out braids, but not Simba. He needed something else to do. I had brought a hand-held tape recorder for recording their voices. I figured I would bring it so everyone back home could hear their cute accents, which I loved so much. I told Simba he could be first.

Simba and Tembeka loved playing with this new toy. Tansy and Nkosi were shyer about it; they acted like they had never spoken on a tape recorder before. They lacked the self-confidence the children had. After it was getting too late I finally had to take it away from them. Tembeka made me promise I wouldn't listen to it until I got home. I promised.

The next day I took Nkosi to his school, then I wanted to get a present for Tansy. I looked at all kinds of things and then just said, "No, I don't know if she'll like it."

Finally I went to pick up the kids. Maybe they could help. They took me to one of their favorite places to shop. It had all kinds of stores, but they weren't any better at deciding than I was. I would say, "How about this?"

"No, I don't know if she'll like it."

"How about this?"

"I don't think so."

We ended up getting her some shoes.

When we went to pick up Nkosi he got in the car all excited. He said, "How would you all like to come to my department party?"

"Are you sure?"

"Yes, because I want you to hear my speech."

"Oh, are you speaking?" This should be interesting I thought. "Is any one else bringing their families?"

"I don't know, they might."

Simba piped in, "And Auntee Peggy too?"

"Yes, Auntee Peggy too."

We all rushed home to get ready; we'd leave Tansy a note. I decided to wait for Tansy. Tembeka wanted to wait with me, so Simba and Nkosi left. When Tansy got home she said she had a cold, and she didn't feel like going, but we went to the party anyway. The party turned out to be a bit more formal than we thought. There were no other children and Tansy didn't feel like mingling. This was a side of Tansy I hadn't seen before. Where did that excited, happy person go? At the party she was as quiet and shy as Nkosi. She didn't laugh at anything. How strange.

After a light, very fancy supper, we sat around in a big circle and chatted. They made a couple of presentations to two of the staff members who were leaving. Each time, they would ask Nkosi if he had anything to add. "No," he would answer, with his head bent down.

After a few more formalities were carried out, I started to wonder if Nkosi really had a speech to give. When they were finishing up and people started saying goodbye, everyone began to walk away. Just then, Nkosi quietly looked up and began to speak, "Yes, there is something I want to say."

One person heard him; it was the man who had been doing all the talking. "Wait, I think Nkosi has something to say."

Everyone turned around to listen, curious as to what Nkosi would have to say. Quietly he stood up, nervously straightening first his pants and then his tie. Everyone in that room knew Nkosi was a man of few words, so he had their total attention. He fidgeted for a few more moments, then cleared his throat, "I would first like to introduce our friend from America. She has been staying with us since the first of the year."

Tansy tapped me on the knee and whispered, "Stand up."

"No way," I whispered back.

"Peggy is from a little town in Utah. Tansy," pointing over to Tansy, "is my wife."

I looked at Tansy; she was blushing.

"My wife and I went to Utah, located in the western United States, back in 1979. I was attending school at the University of Utah. We met Peggy when I went to purchase a black and white television set she was selling."

By now we were both looking at each other and it seemed as if no one else was in the room. He started to let his heart spill out right into mine. There was a long moment of silence. I started to cry because he was crying, then Tansy started to cry.

"Peggy and my wife have continued to write all these years."

Another long pause . . .

"She is very special to us and she has been such a good friend. . . . She will be going back home tonight. . . . In fact, her plane leaves right after the party. . . . I want to take this time to

194

tell her how much we are going to miss her . . . and . . . how much . . ."

Now he got all choked up. He couldn't speak. No one in that room knew me, and no one really knew Nkosi, but there wasn't a dry eye to be seen. Sometimes it means so much more when the words won't come. This big soft-hearted man just stood there sobbing.

By now I was crying so hard I could hardly see. But I felt compelled to speak. I didn't care if I knew these people or not. I stood up. I heard a few voices say, "Speech." The love filling the room at that very moment was so strong; everyone could feel it. I wanted to tell Tansy and that wonderful man shaking over there how much I loved them.

As I began to speak I felt Tansy's hand slip into mine. I don't know how the words even came out, but they did.

"Tansy and Nkosi are some of the finest people you will ever meet. I don't know how I got so lucky, but I thank God every day for bringing them into my life. As you can tell, I think the world of these two. We have shared a most unique friendship . . . and I love them. . . . With all my heart . . . I love them. . . . I felt Tansy squeeze my hand. That did me in. I sat down. I'm not sure why, but everyone started clapping.

Back home we got ready to get on the plane. As I grabbed my suitcases, Tansy noticed I had hooked the zippers on my suitcases together with a bread twist tie. She said, "What is this?"

"Oh, no one would ever try to get into my suitcase."

Then Tansy paid me the best compliment of my life, not even knowing it. She said, "Oh, Peggy, you are just like my mother."

I had come to admire and adore that woman, and here I was being compared with her. She ran to get me some little locks with keys.

At the airport we tried to look as happy as we could. We were giving hugs, and we even asked a man who sat staring at us if he would take our picture.

At last I had to go---not really, but I could not hold my composure any longer. Simba was the one who let down his control. He ran up to me and gave me the biggest kiss. Then he turned all red in the face. We all laughed, except Tansy.

It was dark outside as my plane circled Cape Town once before heading west. My emotions had peaked. I knew I may never be back, and if I could return, it would seem like forever away. What makes some people worth so much to you? I mean the kind that all you have to do is think of them and your heart fills up to overflowing, and then it hurts, literally hurts. Why does it have to hurt?

Okay, so why was Ruby happy all her life?
She believed in giving,
simple, honest, unconditional, giving,
thus making her the receiver.

19

Going Home

After another all-night trip, this time on an airplane, I was in no mood for the news I received upon entering the Miami Airport. I got off the plane, and they announced that my flight home was cancelled due to the airline strike.

They started herding us like cattle into lines to wait until someone could help us. Waiting in line for hours is never anyone's idea of fun, but at four in the morning after spending all night on a plane, you can imagine what tempers were like.

When I finally got to speak with an attendant, she informed me there were no flights going to Salt Lake City. I would have to catch a connecting flight and there were no connecting flights to Salt Lake. I said, "Have you tried all of the cities close to Salt Lake?"

I thought if all else failed, my husband would drive over and pick me up.

"Name some of them for me."

"Okay, how about Denver?"

"No."

"Los Angeles?"

"Nothing."

"Portland, Phoenix, Boise, Dallas?"

No luck. She kept trying for what seemed like hours. People all around me were equally upset. Tempers were raging, frustrations mounting, some people were even in tears, and it was the poor ladies behind those desks that had to take the brunt of all this confusion.

Finally the gal that was helping me said she found a cancellation. She booked me from Miami to Denver, Denver to Salt Lake. Yes! I was going home at last. By now it was six a.m. and my next flight didn't leave until two. I still had eight hours to kill, but at least I had a flight---and I was going home.

While I was sitting in the Burger King having breakfast I started talking to a women about my trip. She was fascinated to hear about Africa. But she caught me off guard when she said, "Weren't you afraid to go to Africa?"

I explained to her that there wasn't really anything to be afraid of. Then I sat down and started to write a thank-you note to Tansy and Nkosi. Once again my thoughts turned to Africa. This time to the man I met in Namibia. What if I could help him get his gold mine going? I have heard some people say, "Why should we help uncivilized people become civilized? Aren't we doing them more harm than good? What makes us so egotistical that we think our way is better?"

To that I would say, who likes to drink dirty water? Who likes to be cold all night? Who likes to be sick with a fever and have not even an aspirin to take? Who likes to be hungry? Who of us would go without hot water? These are basic needs; these are comforts.

Is it right that any man, in this day and age, should not have at least his basic needs met? This is the kind of "civilized" that people need. Perhaps since we are so far above those simple needs we have forgotten, or never even knew, what it was like to not have them. This is the only reason I would want to help Lweedo and his family.

But what about the children? My mind went back to my conversation with Tansy as I was helping her take out her braids. Perhaps small children, like the small boys I saw in the township just sitting in the dirt having fun playing with bones, have never known a better life. It doesn't take much to keep small children happy. But those older school children, the ones who have been taught in a primary school, have been given a taste and then reality hits. Many dream of going on, but the reality is that there is only one university in Zimbabwe, and most could not afford to go anyway.

You can take any state in the United States and you will find many good colleges and universities. In my home state alone there are nearly a dozen colleges and universities. Talk about fair, talk about America, the land of opportunity, not having enough chances for their poor. If there is one thing we have---that they only dream of---it's opportunity.

Okay, so what. Why do I care about black people in Africa? My mind was struggling with itself. Then I remembered the beauty. Africa holds some of the world's most fantastic places. When I got back to Cape Town I looked up Liberia on the internet. I was curious to see if what Lweendo had told me was true. This is what I read.

"At first glance, you might not think Liberia has made much progress since its long civil war ended in 1996. Monrovia, the capital, still bears the fresh scars of a war zone. But the country is finally pulling itself together and exiles are returning. Liberia is still not an appealing destination for the average traveler. The level of poverty and inconvenience would probably horrify a first-time visitor to Africa. But if conditions remain stable, adventurous travelers interested in experiencing wildlife in an unusual, nonsafari setting may want to consider a visit to the country's top attraction: Sapo National Park, a dense tropical rain forest filled with chimpanzees, elephants, pygmy hippos, leopards, and other rare animals and birds."

When I first read this I wanted to go help Lweendo with his gold. But the sad truth is that even the leaders in these countries are uneducated. Many governments remain very unstable and investments in such countries are too risky. Until they get highly educated men in leadership positions, none of us will be able to see many of Africa's wonders.

So what can we do? What can I do? The answers lie in the children and in educating them.

My thoughts were interrupted when a woman sitting next to me broke in. "Excuse me, may I borrow a piece of your paper?"

I looked over to the woman sitting next to me, her husband asleep on the chair next to her. I replied, "Sure."

She then asked, "Where are you from?"

"Salt Lake City."

"Oh, that's where we are going. Do you ski?"

"Yes."

"Were you staying in Miami?"

"No, I was staying with some friends in South Africa."

"South Africa?"

"Yes. Do you know much about South Africa?"

"No, nothing. But I have always wanted to know more about Africa."

So I started to tell her a little about my trip. Right in the middle of my story, she interrupted, "Oh, weren't you scared?"

The exact same thing happened to me on my flight from Denver to Salt Lake. A man started talking to me about his trip. Then he asked about my trip. Suddenly he blurted in, "Weren't you scared to be in Africa?"

By now it began to occur to me that everyone had the idea that Africans were some barbaric creatures, preying off innocent people, or something. I had just spent ten hours in the Miami Airport. I can honestly say that I was more scared to go outside and walk down the streets of Miami than I ever was in Namibia, Zimbabwe, Botswana, or Zambia.

My mind kind of went into a blur. I was no longer listening to his words. Oh, I could see him talking, but in front of me now I saw the smiling faces of Nkosi, Simba, Mapenzi, Mugunda, Teiso, and Lweendo. Never did I fear for my life. They were my friends. For every bad person in the world there are hundreds of good people and you find good and bad no matter where you go.

True, Africa has had a very bad reputation, but was it just a coincidence that I had met only the good?

Now the man sitting next to me saw that I was not listening, so he turned back to his laptop computer. That's when I remembered the tape recorder on which I had the Manjanis record a message to my family. Tembeka had told me not to listen to it until I got home, but I was curious, so I got it out.

First I heard little Simba singing a Michael Jackson song to me. Then Tembeka came on, "Jessica, Halee, Jenny, Kellie, I want to tell you thank you for letting your mum come to see us." Then she kind of whispered the rest.

"I want to tell your mum: it was *w-o-n-d-e-r-f-u-l* . . . *w-o-n-d-e-r-f-u-l!*"

"Yes, Tembeka, it was wonderful!"

THE END

THE CHILDREN

THE CHILDREN

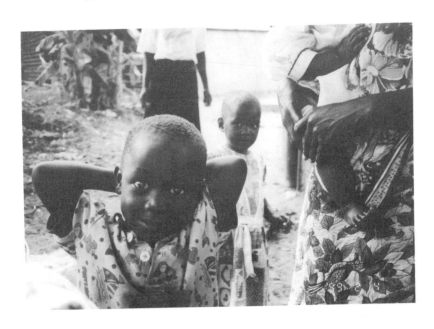

Other's will believe in you,
When you believe in yourself.

Author's Note

When I got back home, and got back into my routine, my life was pretty much as I had left it. Everything seemed the same, only I was not. I couldn't get the problems of Africa out of my mind. I know the problems I saw are Universal, and you can find people living in fear no matter where you go, but in my simplistic mind I still believe Love is the answer.

If you have read my book you know that I believe in the good found in each of us. And that there is more good than evil in the world. It seems that the good works go on quietly and that most people don't even know they are going on at all, but if we want to see miracles happen and changes made, changes which make a real difference in peoples lives then our strength lies in our numbers.

It was not my intention, nor will it ever be my intention to point fingers at anyone. I told this story exactly how I saw it. The two things which have disturbed me the most since I got home are; first that the Zambian dollar in the one year since I have been home has dropped in value even double from what it was, it has gone from 400 to one to now 800 to one. Second, that the country of Liberia is so unsafe I can find no one willing to go in and help Lweendo's family for fear of their own life. I can see that the blacks need the whites just as much as the whites need the blacks. I hope these situations can improve, but they will only improve if we the majority of feeling sensitive people unite to make the difference. If my one small voice can help at all then let it be heard by sending out a plea. I know that it is easier for an outsider to look on to the problems and come up with solutions than for the ones who are actually caught up in the problems. But please at least consider my plea.

First to the whites, who hold in their hands the financial as well as the emotional ability to restore self-esteem to a people struggling to find who they really are, and struggling to like themselves for being who they are. They should be treated as equal, all of God's children deserve that.

Second to the blacks, who, if they are willing to trust the whites, not all of the whites want to push them aside, become educated, working with the modern world instead of against it, helping their children to see the importance of an education. Then last, to stop the degrading and hateful acts of a few, who practice hostility towards others.

If things go on as they have, then fear will continue to abound and no progress can be made.

"Okay," you say, "how can I help? We want to show the black people in Africa we care." Here is where the future starts to look brighter, I could not forget the faces of the children. Their laughter, their innocence, their quest for a happy future, reality has not yet hit them and if we can help it won't have to. Many people wonder and are overwhelmed at the mere thought where do we start? The truth is we must start somewhere. In fact if each person in this world found just one thing they could do to help, we'd all start seeing the miracles happen. If we combine the children, with the key, education . . . then we begin to find the answers.

The more I thought about it, the more I knew. First I would have to get the message out. I tried to write a book, I hoped it would be warm and enjoyable yet at the same time enlightening. After tackling that hurdle, (I hope), I wish to let you in on my dream. This story of my dear friends is only the beginning. Now it's up to each of you to become part of that dream.

I had to change many of the names in this book for protection purposes. But Tansy's mother, Wynoma's real name is Veronica Chipendo. Since she has now passed away and I felt this would be safe to say. I have set up a fund called the "Zambia's Veronica Chipendo Scholarship Fund" also using Tansy's mother's real name. I thought this was only fitting.

Veronica is my hero. She in her quiet life gave everything she had, and she had very little, especially when it came to material possessions. The education she gave her children can never be measured. It was only a tiny seed planted where it could begin to grow. It blessed her life because Tansy said, "My mother died a happy woman. Just before she died she saw her last child graduate from nursing school. That completed her goal of seeing each of her children complete their education past their primary schooling."

I will not make a dime off of this book. No, my reward will be far greater than money. All profits from this book will go into the scholarship fund. Then eager students in Zambia who want to attend a university but find it impossible, can send me a picture of themselves, a story of why they want to go, and what they hope to accomplish there. I will choose the most determined (a difficult task, I'm sure) and give them a full scholarship. Now you see the dream start to unfold. In my mind I can see the excited faces of those students as we make their dream become a reality, thus making my dream become a reality.

Thank you for the purchase of this book. If you wish to purchase more books please request them at your local bookstore. For more information on ordering books or making charitable donations to Zambia's Veronica Chipendo Scholarship Fund, please write to the following address:

Zambia's Veronica Chipendo Scholarship Fund
P.O. Box 515
Brigham City, Utah
84302-0515

You may purchase as many books as you would like. Please include the purchase price plus one dollar per book for shipping and handling. Thank you once again and I hope you have enjoyed the book.